Origins
of the Yoga Postures in
Ancient Egypt

Cruzian Mystic Books / Sema Institute of Yoga
P.O.Box 570459
Miami, Florida, 33257
(305) 378-6253 Fax: (305) 378-6253

© 2006 By Reginald Muata Abhaya Ashby

The author is available for group lectures and individual counseling. For further information contact the publisher.

Ashby, Muata
The African Origins of Hatha Yoga ISBN: 1-884564-60-7

Temple of Shetaut Neter-Aset
INTERNET ADDRESS: www.Egyptianyoga.com
E-MAIL ADDRESS: Semayoga@aol.com

About the Author

Mr. Ashby began studies in the area of religion and philosophy and achieved doctorates in these areas while at the same time he began to collect his research into what would later become several books on the subject of the African History, religion and ethics, world mythology, origins of Yoga Philosophy and practice in ancient Africa (Ancient Egypt/Nubia) and also the origins of Christian Mysticism in Ancient Egypt. He has extensively studied mystical religious traditions from around the world and is an accomplished lecturer, musician, artist, poet, painter, screenwriter, playwright and author of over 25 books on yoga philosophy, religious philosophy and social philosophy based on ancient African principles. A leading advocate of the concept of the existence of advanced social and religious philosophy in ancient Africa comparable to the Eastern traditions such as Vedanta, Buddhism, Confucianism and Taoism, he has lectured and written extensively on the correlations of these with ancient African religion and philosophy.

Muata Abhaya Ashby holds a Doctor of Philosophy Degree in Religion, and a Doctor of Divinity Degree in Holistic Health and a Masters Degree in Liberal Arts and Religious Studies. He is also a Pastoral Counselor and Teacher of Yoga Philosophy and Discipline. Dr. Ashby received his Doctor of Divinity Degree from and is an adjunct faculty member of Florida International University and the American Institute of Holistic Theology. Dr. Ashby is a certified as a PREP Relationship Counselor. Dr. Ashby has been an independent researcher and practitioner of Egyptian Yoga, Indian Yoga, Chinese Yoga, Buddhism and mystical psychology as well as Christian Mysticism. Dr. Ashby has engaged in Post Graduate research in advanced Jnana, Bhakti and Kundalini Yogas at the Yoga Research Foundation.

Dr. Ashby began his research into the spiritual philosophy of Ancient Egypt and India and noticed correlations in the culture and arts of the two countries. This was the catalyst for a successful book series on the subject called "Egyptian Yoga". Since 1999 he has researched Ancient Egyptian musical theory and created a series of musical compositions which explore this unique area of music from ancient Africa and its connection to world music.

TABLE OF CONTENTS

Foreword:

Greetings,

This book is a compilation of several sections of a larger work, a book by the name of *African Origins of Civilization, Religion, Yoga Mysticism and Ethics Philosophy.* It is one of several compiled short volumes that has been compiled so as to facilitate access to specific subjects contained in the larger work which is over 680 pages long. These short and small volumes have been specifically designed to cover one subject in a brief and low cost format. This volume also contains some additional information not contained in the previous work.

This subject of this present volume, *The Ancient Egyptian Origins of Yoga Postures,* formed one subject in the larger works, *African Origins of Civilization Religion, Yoga Mysticism and Ethics Philosophy* and the Book *Egypt and India* is the section of the book *African Origins of Civilization.* Those works contain the collection of all correlations between Ancient Egypt and India. It was felt that this subject needed to be discussed more directly, being treated in one volume, as opposed to being contained in the larger work along with other subjects, because even in the early 21st century, the idea persists that the Yoga and specifically, Yoga Postures, were invented and developed only in India. The Ancient Egyptians were peoples originally from Africa who were, in ancient times, colonists in India. Therefore it is no surprise that many Indian traditions including religious and Yogic, would be found earlier in Ancient Egypt. Yet there is ample evidence from ancient writings and perhaps more importantly, iconographical evidences from the Ancient Egyptians themselves and the Indians themselves that prove the connection between Ancient Egypt and India as well as the existence of a discipline of Yoga Postures in Ancient Egypt long before its practice in India. This handy volume has been designed to be accessible to young adults and all others who would like to have an easy reference with documentation on this important subject. This is an important subject because the frame of reference with which we look at a culture depends strongly on our conceptions about its origins. In this case, if we look at the Ancient Egyptians as Asiatic peoples we would treat them and their culture in one way. If we see them as Africans we not only see them in a different light but we also must ascribe Africa with a glorious legacy that matches any other culture in human history. We would also look at the culture and philosophies of the Ancient Egyptians as having African insights instead of Asiatic ones. Those insights inform our knowledge bout other African traditions and we can also begin to understand in a deeper way the effect of Ancient Egyptian culture on African culture and also on the Asiatic as well. When we discover the deeper and more ancient practice of the postures system in Ancient Egypt that was called "Hatha Yoga" in India, we are able to find a new and expanded understanding of the practice that constitutes a discipline of spiritual practice that informs and revitalizes the Indian practices as well as all spiritual disciplines.

Preface: What is Yoga?

Above: Hatha Yogi from the early 20th century

Most people in the Western countries think of yoga as the practice of strange physical postures or a meditating yogi in some strange contorted posture. The practice of physical postures is actually only a small part of the overall Yoga practice. Yet many people focus on that alone as the whole of the practice, thereby missing out on and usually misunderstanding the true purpose and application of the disciplines of the practice of Yoga. The term "Hatha Yoga" means Forceful Yoga". Specifically, it means yoga, that is, the movement of union of the lower self with the higher, that is artificially enhanced through certain postures. Yoga is the practice of mental, physical and spiritual disciplines which lead to self-control and self-discovery by purifying the mind, body and spirit, so as to discover the deeper spiritual essence which lies within every human being and object in the universe. In essence, the goal of Yoga practice is to unite or *yoke* one's individual consciousness with Universal or Cosmic consciousness. Therefore, Ancient Egyptian religious practice, especially in terms of the rituals and other practices of the Ancient Egyptian Temple system known as *Shetaut Neter* (the way of the hidden Supreme Being), also known in Ancient times as *Smai Tawi* "Egyptian Yoga," should as well be considered as universal streams of self-knowledge philosophy which influenced and inspired the great religions and philosophers to this day. In this sense, religion, in its purest form, is also a Yoga system, as it seeks to reunite the soul with its true and original source, God. In broad terms, any spiritual movement or discipline that brings one closer to self-knowledge is a "Yogic" movement.

The literal meaning of the word YOGA is to *"YOKE"* or to *"LINK"* back. The implication is: to link back individual consciousness to its original source, the original essence, that which transcends all mental and intellectual attempts at comprehension, but which is the essential nature of everything in CREATION: Universal Consciousness. In a broad sense Yoga is any process which helps one to achieve liberation or freedom from the bondage of human existence. So whenever you engage in any activity with the goal of promoting the discovery of your true self, be it studying the wisdom teachings, practicing them in daily life, practicing exercises to keep the mind and body healthy for meditation, rituals to lead the mind toward the divine or meditation on the divine, you are practicing yoga. If the goal is to help you to discover your essential nature as one with God or the Supreme Being or Consciousness, then it is yoga.

The disciplines of Yoga fall under five major categories. These are: *Yoga of Wisdom, Yoga of Devotional love, Yoga of Meditation, Tantric Yoga* and *Yoga of Selfless Action.* Within these categories there are subsidiary forms which are part of the main disciplines. The important point to remember is that all aspects of yoga can and should be used in an integral fashion to effect an efficient and harmonized spiritual movement in the practitioner. Therefore, while there may be an area of special emphasis, other elements are bound to become part of the yoga program as needed. For example, while a yogin may place emphasis on the yoga of wisdom, they may also practice devotional yoga and meditation yoga along with the wisdom studies.

So the practice of any discipline that leads to oneness with Supreme Consciousness is called Yoga. If you study, rationalize and reflect upon the teachings, you are practicing *Yoga of Wisdom.* If you meditate upon the teachings and your Higher Self, you are practicing *Yoga of Meditation.* If you practice rituals which identify you with your spiritual nature, you are practicing *Yoga of Ritual Identification.* If you develop your physical nature and psychic energy centers, you are practicing *Serpent Power* (*Kundalini or Uraeus*) *Yoga.* If you practice living according to the teachings of ethical behavior and selflessness, you are practicing *Yoga of Action* in daily life. If you practice turning your attention toward the Divine by developing love for the Divine, you are practicing *Devotional Yoga* or *Yoga of Divine Love.* The practitioner of yoga is called a yogin (male practitioner) or yogini (female practitioner) and one who has attained the culmination of yoga is also called a yogi. In this manner yoga has been developed into many disciplines which may be used in an integral fashion to achieve the same goal: Enlightenment. Enlightenment is the state of consciousness of complete harmony of mind, body and spirit wherein one discovers one's true identity and union with the Divine. Enlightenment also implies the discovery of one's innermost Self, the immortal and eternal elements of one's being beyond the mortal and transitory human personality and body. Therefore, the aspirant should learn about all of the paths of yoga and choose those elements which best suit his/her personality or practice them all in an integral, balanced way.

Advancement in Yoga is dependent on the desire of the individual to put forth his/her effort in the direction toward self-improvement under proper guidance. In this way, the negative karma of the past which has created the present conditions can be destroyed in order to create prosperity and spiritual emancipation.

The main recognized forms of Yoga disciplines are:

- *Yoga of Wisdom,*
- *Yoga of Devotional Love,*
- *Yoga of Meditation,*
    - *Physical Postures Yoga- {Hatha Yoga}*
- *Yoga of Selfless Action,*
- *Tantric Yoga*
    - *Serpent Power Yoga*

The diagram below shows the relationship between the Yoga disciplines and the path of mystical religion (religion practiced in its three complete steps: 1st receiving the myth {knowledge}, 2nd practicing the rituals of the myth {following the teachings of the myth} and 3rd entering into a mystical experience {becoming one with the central figure of the myth}).

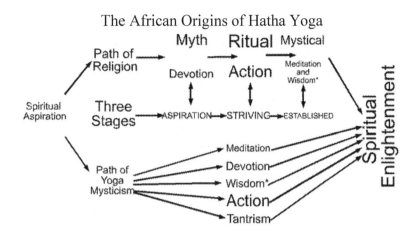

The African Origins of Hatha Yoga

The disciplines of Yoga fall under five major categories. These are: *Yoga of Wisdom, Yoga of Devotional Love, Yoga of Meditation, Tantric Yoga* and *Yoga of Selfless Action.* When these disciplines are practiced in a harmonized manner this practice is called "Integral Yoga." Within these categories there are subsidiary forms which are part of the main disciplines. The emphasis in the Kamitan Asarian (Osirian) Myth is on the Yoga of Wisdom, Yoga of Devotional Love and Yoga of Selfless Action. The important point to remember is that all aspects of Yoga can and should be used in an integral fashion to effect an efficient and harmonized spiritual movement in the practitioner. Therefore, while there may be an area of special emphasis, other elements are bound to become part of the Yoga program as needed. For example, while a Yogin (practitioner of Yoga, aspirant, initiate) may place emphasis on the Yoga of Wisdom, they may also practice Devotional Yoga and Meditation Yoga along with the wisdom studies. So the practice of any discipline that leads to oneness with Supreme Consciousness can be called Yoga. If you study, rationalize and reflect upon the teachings, you are practicing *Yoga of Wisdom.* If you meditate upon the teachings and your Higher Self, you are practicing *Yoga of Meditation.*

Thus, whether or not you refer to it as such, if you practice rituals which identify you with your spiritual nature, you are practicing *Yoga of Ritual Identification* (which is part of the Yoga of Wisdom {Kamitan-Rekh, Indian-Jnana} and the Yoga of Devotional Love {Kamitan-Ushet, Indian-Bhakti} of the Divine). If you develop your physical nature and psychic energy centers, you are practicing *Serpent Power* (Kamitan-*Uraeus* or Indian-*Kundalini*) *Yoga* (which is part of Tantric Yoga). If you practice living according to the teachings of ethical behavior and selflessness, you are practicing *Yoga of Action* (Kamitan-Maat, Indian-Karma) in daily life. If you practice turning your attention towards the Divine by developing love for the Divine, then it is called *Devotional Yoga* or *Yoga of Divine Love.* The practitioner of Yoga is called a Yogin (male practitioner) or Yogini (female practitioner), or the term "Yogi" may be used to refer to either a female or male practitioner in general terms. One who has attained the culmination of Yoga (union with the Divine) is also called a Yogi. In this manner, Yoga has been developed into many disciplines which may be used in an integral fashion to achieve the same goal: Enlightenment. Therefore, the aspirant is to learn about all of the paths of Yoga and choose those elements which best suit {his/her} personality or practice them all in an integral, balanced way.

Enlightenment is the term used to describe the highest level of spiritual awakening. It means attaining such a level of spiritual awareness that one discovers the underlying unity of the entire universe as well as the fact that the source of all creation is the same source from which the innermost Self within every human heart arises.

"As one can ascend to the top of a house by means of a ladder or a tree or a staircase or a rope, so diverse are the ways and means to approach God, and every religion in the world shows one of these ways."

-Ramakrishna (1836-1886)

9

Receptivity to The Discussion About The Origins of Yoga

The authors of the book *In Search of the Cradle of Civilization,* 1995, p. 15, co-authored by Georg Feuerstein, David Frawley, and Subhash Kak. called for a *"critical reexamination"* into the origins of Yoga. However, the point was also made that in view of the previous statements by the authors , the reader's first impression might be that there is a proclivity towards one point of view, which suggests a contradiction with the following statement from the same book that ignores the possibility of the origins of Yoga outside of India and turns the attention solely towards the Vedas.

> "The time is ripe for a critical reexamination of the question of the origin of Yoga. In looking for the roots of Yoga in the Vedas, we must first of all rid ourselves of the tendency to indulge in what scholars call arguments ex silentio; that is, to favor a particular point of view because of the absence of contrary evidence. For instance, we might argue that, because the original Pledge of Allegiance did not contain the phrase "one nation under God," the American people were irreligious prior to 1954 when the Pledge was changed by an Act of Congress. This is dearly absurd, and yet this kind of argument is frequently resorted to by scholars, especially when defending cherished positions." p.173[1]

There is a feeling among many who are interested in Yoga philosophy as it was practiced in Ancient Egypt and India that there is a refusal by many European and North Indian scholars to acknowledge the growing mountain of evidences that have been cited in this and other volumes. Two factors have been broached to explain this apparent rebuke. It has been charged, for example, that while many practitioners and scholars of Yoga as it developed in India and later developed in the West espouse a "universalistic" perspective as to the nature of Yoga, portraying it as a phenomenon that has existed in all cultures from the beginning of civilization or as a common human need expressed by people who do not follow the Indian path, they present also in many of their statements a subtle pride in claiming the Indian origin, and Indian perfection of the art, thus relegating, by implication, other forms of spiritual practice, which might be considered "Yogically" based but not originating in India as primitive, uncivilized or meek in comparison to Indian Yoga, thereby undermining and demeaning them.

The inference is also that others claiming to practice "Yoga" outside of the Indian framework for the word and practice are actually doing something else that is alien or at least other than the Indian concepts and disciplines. Thus, by implication, the custodians of that specialty (Indian Yoga) become the purveyors as well as the sole authorities on it, and at the same time ensnaring themselves in the web of egoism spun by pride, ignorance and misunderstanding, for many such statements are a backlash against years of Western denigration of Eastern spirituality. Some have suggested the factor that many European and Indian scholars feel a sense of superiority due to their association with the Vedic-Sanskrit tradition, viewing it as the source of civilization. The pride of having a supposedly advanced literary culture gives way to narcissism and inflated egos. This understandably can lead to social castes systems placing the purveyors of the supposedly high literature at the top of the social order. It is also understandable how this conceit can lead to the great problems which follows caste systems, the attendant racism and sexism.

Others have suggested that a racist mentality has developed among some scholars, based on their association with racist Europeans and Arabs. This feeling has, in a subtle way, caused many north Indian scholars (who are of lighter complexion than their southern counterparts) to promote an "Aryan" world view as opposed to a "Dravidian" world view or the possibility of any outside influence on the Vedic tradition as opposed to an indigenous development or influence. This position remains intransigent, even after examining some of the evidences which have been presented by African and Indian scholars supporting the influence of Dravidian culture and existence of Yoga practices in Ancient Egypt as well as contact and cultural exchange between

Ancient Egypt and Northern as well as Southern India both before and after the emergence of Aryan culture and Yoga philosophy in India.

Indologists on the Origins of Yoga

In reference to the origins of Yoga, the authors of the book *In Search of the Cradle of Civilization,* by Georg Feuerstein, David Frawley, and Subhash Kak assert the following on Pages 170-171. (Highlighted portions by Ashby)

"The Hindus have traditionally *looked to* the archaic *Vedas* as the seedbed of the later Yoga tradition.* The Vedic seers are honored as illumined sages who passed down the secrets of meditation and higher consciousness to subsequent generations of spiritual practitioners. Reflecting this idea, the teachers of the school of Classical Yoga, embodied in the *Yoga-Sutra of* Patanjali and his commentators, not only employ Vedic concepts in their teachings but also speak of their tradition as thoroughly Vedic."
*See, e.g., D. Frawley, *Gods, Sages and Kings: Vedic Secrets of Civilization* (Salt Lake City, UT: Passage Press, 1991), pp.203-236

"The term *Yoga* itself first occurs in the *Rig-Veda, but* does not yet have its later technical connotation. In many instances, it simply means "application",** The word *Yoga* is one of the most flexible terms *of* the Sanskrit language and therefore has been used in many diverse contexts, in addition to its specific philosophical meaning. In the technical sense of "spiritual discipline," the term *Yoga* first made its appearance in the *Taittiriya-Upanishad,* a work belonging possibly to the era around 1000 B.C. or even earlier."
**See, e.g., *Rig-Veda* 1.5.3; 1.30.11; X.114.9. The term *yogya and yojana* apparently are used as synonyms of *Yoga.*

Many of modern India's Yoga adepts believe that the *Vedas* contain the original teachings of Yoga.

The statements above show that most practitioners of Yoga in India look to the Vedas as the source or origin of the tradition. However, even the prominent Indologists, Georg Feuerstein, David Frawley, and Subhash Kak, admit that the use of the term is just that, the use of the term and it does not relate to what we know of today as the tradition and technology of Yoga, which the authors say began with the Upanishads. Yet there is persistence in upholding the Vedic origins and the use of the word itself as synonymous with the concept is implied. We must be reminded that belief in a tradition does not mean that the tradition is real and therefore, without a direct philosophical link, the Yogic tradition of India cannot be taken further back than the Upanishadic period. It is as if the terms of the Vedas such as Yoga, Brahman, Dharma, Maya and others were taken by the Upanishadic sages and redefined to conform to the high philosophy which we have come to recognize today as Yoga.

The Kamitan Ancient Egyptian) Yoga and Universal Practice of Yoga

yo·ga (yō′gə) *n.* **1.** A Hindu discipline aimed at training the consciousness for a state of perfect spiritual insight and tranquility. **2.** A system of exercises practiced as part of this discipline to promote control of the body and mind. – **yo′gic** (-gĭk) *adj.*

—American Heritage Dictionary

The pervasiveness of the Sanskrit term "Yoga" from India has become so well known that it has been added to the Western lexicons. This pervasiveness has also promoted the idea that Yoga originated or was invented in India. In the case of the origins of Indian Yoga, many scholars and world renowned spiritual masters have recognized the strong connections between India and Ancient Africa, namely Joseph Campbell, R.A. Schwaller de Lubicz, Omraam Mikhael Aivanhov, and Swami Sivananda Radha. However, what they stated amounted to a few pieces of a larger puzzle which until now had not been pursued in an extensive and comprehensive manner. What makes the this volume important is that attempts to put those pieces together and goes further to show that Kamitan (Ancient Egyptian) Yoga, the Yoga practice of Ancient Africa, is a living, breathing spiritual discipline that is being followed today and which has something substantial to contribute to modern day Yogic culture and to the upliftment of humanity. Some people in the general Yogic community, who up to now, have only been aware of the Indian Yoga legacy have been surprised and delighted to discover the Kamitan Yoga legacy, while others have had their closely but sentimentally held notions about Yoga and Yoga philosophy challenged. As discussed in the previous section, some many people have come to regard Yoga is a proprietary commodity which is owned by East-Indians, since they see this as the origin. When the nature and essence of what Yoga is, is fully understood, its source as a universal human spiritual movement becomes clear. Yet there are correlations between Ancient Egyptian "Sema" and Indian "Yoga" that go beyond simple similarities based on universal practices among all human beings around the world.

The Debate On The Question Of The Origins Of Yoga

In reference to the question of the origins of Yoga, there has been a growing interest into exploring certain apparent correlations between the form of spirituality that was practiced in Ancient Egypt and that which is commonly referred to as Yoga mysticism of India. Again, here as well many Western Indologist as well as lay peoples ascribe the origin of Yoga to India simply because it is India where the practice expanded to the rest of the world under the name which it is known today.

The seemingly dogmatic approach to the study of Hindu history and Yoga, as expressed by many Eurocentrists and Indologists presented earlier, has led to the promotion, by some, of the idea that Yoga philosophy emerged in India simply because the word Yoga is a Sanskrit term.[2] This is like saying that a rose that grows in South America cannot be a rose because the South Americans do not use the term "rose" from the English language which is common to North America or England. Further, in reference to Yoga, if this view is taken, then we cannot conclude that Yoga emerged as a development of Ancient India, but was a product of outside influence

12

since the word does not appear in India until the introduction of the Sanskrit language in 1,500 B.C.E. This would mean that until it appears in the Rig Veda[3] one cannot say that Yoga "existed" at all in India since the term did not yet exist. In other words, it appeared out of nowhere or it came from outside India and it developed elsewhere. A deep philosophical discipline such as Yoga cannot appear without a long process of development and refinement unless one believes in "spontaneous generation." Moreover, when the use of the term "Yoga" in the Rig Veda is examined, it simply means to yoke, as in attaching something, an object like a cart, to something else, a horse for example. The great mystical philosophy which Indian Yoga has come to be known for, uniting the individual with the Universal, did not become associated with the term until the appearance of the *Taittiriya Upanishad, c.* 1,000-800 B.C.E. This argument therefore means that no Yoga was practiced anywhere (even in India) as a mystical philosophy until 1,000 B.C.E. in India at the earliest.

The problem with this argument is obvious. It would appear that in an attempt to appropriate the philosophy of Yoga as having an "Indian only" origin, many scholars as well as ignorant lay people of Indian and non-Indian origin have sought to equate the philosophy of Yoga with the appearance of the Sanskrit word. This endeavor has revealed the aforementioned inconsistency, as we know that something cannot come from nothing. Yoga did not appear out of nowhere but from the early developments of sages and saints. Otherwise we would have to also conclude that gravity did not exist until Isaac Newton named the force (gravity) that holds human beings on earth and prevents them from flying off into space! Further, this would be like saying that a mystic who practices the mystical disciplines (meditation, wisdom, devotion and right action) in America could not meet a practitioner of mysticism in Africa and realize that they have the same goals and use the same techniques for attaining higher consciousness simply because they do not use the same terms to describe what they do, or that if two such individuals were to meet they could not relate to each other or would not "compare notes," that is, to consider or describe their respective systems of spirituality as similar, equal, or analogous. They would not be able to liken or examine each other's systems of spirituality in order to note the similarities or differences and perhaps even merge or adopt some technique or philosophical understanding from each other that may seem useful.

Yogic philosophy and the Yogic impetus in humankind is nothing more than the innate desire to experience unbounded peace and joy and the pursuit of self-knowledge. It is a birthright of humanity and its most common and important instinct. Therefore, Yoga, regardless of the name it has been given in a particular culture, is the philosophy and technology for attaining spiritual enlightenment, the union of the Lower and Higher nature. Therefore, Yoga cannot be considered as a linguistic term but as a natural cultural expression of the desire to discover the heights of human experience. As this desire is common to all human beings, then it follows that all cultures, in all periods where civilization had reached a point where the basic necessities of life had been met, developed a form of technology and philosophy of self-discovery. Therefore, it is proper to use the term "Yoga" when describing the technology and philosophy of Yoga (main disciplines: meditation, wisdom, devotion and right action), which the word has come to be associated with in and outside of India through the popularity of the Sanskrit term. So we can now speak of the form or style of the technology and philosophy of meditating, understanding, worshipping and promoting virtue, as it developed in Christianity and call it "Christian Yoga," and as it developed in Ancient Egypt and call it "Egyptian or Kamitan Yoga." However, just because this technology and philosophy exists in two cultures one cannot say that they are related or that they have a common origin. Again, this is because while two separate cultures may have the same goal, their manner of pursuing that goal will usually be different due to the diverse possibilities that the world offers for folkloric developments. Like the late great Hindu saint, Ramakrishna said, *"God is like a lake and the religions are like paths to that lake which come from all directions."* Only when we see certain correlations in various factors of cultural expression, and these can be backed up by evidence of prior contact, can we venture to assert that such a connection is present.

In the book *In Search of the Cradle of Civilization,* there is an admission that the Vedas do not incorporate *"technical Yoga practices"* and that they are not trying to *"communicate facts but spiritual meanings"* and that therefore, they are *"composed in a highly symbolic language."* Myth is a fluid language, and when two different cultures come into contact, it will be easier to exchange metaphor and symbols, which constitute the essential expressions of myth. Yoga is also a spiritual philosophy that encompasses myth, metaphor and symbol to convey the transcendental path to discover the *Absolute.* It accomplishes this with the use of myth, and symbolic language but it is based on the same mystical principles but may be presented through different folk myths. While some of the disciplines of Yoga contain technical language this should not be taken to mean that there is one pathway, as there are many paths. So technical language may be used in a particular path and at the same time it does not negate others. Conversely, the language of one culture does not hamper the practice of the same religion in another. Otherwise one could only expect to see Buddhists who speak the language that Buddha spoke, or Christians who speak the language that Jesus spoke, and so on.

In recent months, the leading English language Yoga magazines in the West have run articles on *Buddhist Yoga, Chinese Yoga, Yoga of the Ancient Hebrews, Yoganics, Aikido- the Yoga of Combat, and one called The New Yoga: America is Reinventing the Practice But is it Still Yoga?*[4] And another related to an *"Egyptian Yogi"*[5] called Plotinus. For a student of Yoga literature it will be quickly apparent that these disciplines, whatever they may be, are not part of the history of the Vedas so why have they received sufficient attention to merit an article and be called Yoga? Also, why has the Egyptian practice of Yoga been overlooked in such articles even though evidences of the practice of Yoga in Egypt have been presented? We are referring to yoga practices that appear to be direct borrowings from Ancient Egypt and not just general yogic philosophies that appear in many places around the world.

Plotinus was born in Egypt, and he followed the teachings of Plato and Pythagoras. He also taught asceticism in (70-205 A.C.E.). However, he came very late in the history of Yoga and while the article shows that these philosophies are compatible with Yoga, it stresses the possibility that there was some contact by which he might have learned some basic teachings from Indian Yogis. There is no mention of the fact that according to the Greek Classical writers, Plato and Pythagoras learned their philosophy from the Ancient Egyptian sages who received their knowledge in an unbroken line of initiation from the time thousands of years before the Indus valley civilization arose, a factor confirmed by the Greeks themselves.

> "This is also confirmed by the most learned of Greeks such as Solon, Thales, Plato, Eudoxus, Pythagoras, and as some say, even Lycurgus going to Egypt and conversing with the priests; of whom they say Euxodus was a hearer of Chonuphis of Memphis,[6] Solon of Sonchis of Sais,[7] and Pythagoras of Oenuphis of Heliopolis.[8]"
>
> -Plutarch, Morals, 10
> (c. 46-120 AD),
> Greek author/Initiate of Isis.

The publication of perhaps frivolous articles and the conspicuous omission of a serious treatment of Kamitan (Egyptian) Yoga as an ancient tradition denotes the incapacity to confront the issue which may possibly necessitate the rethinking of the history of Yoga and consequently the manner in which the message, heritage and legacy of Yoga is transmitted to the West. It is one thing to convince oneself that Yoga has an Indian only background, and then become an authority on that framework to focus on Mesopotamia or Egypt and espouse a rigid conservative traditionalistic view. From this standpoint it would be quite comfortable to look at other traditions that may have some similar aspects and even consider these as containing some aspect of Yoga, but underlying this treatment is a "centrist" point of view which does not take these "new" traditions seriously. For someone with this notion it will be quite another thing entirely to fully and honestly consider new information that point to not only deeper roots of Yoga but also a living breathing practice of the art outside of the traditionalist view. It would be like realizing an error as well as possibly losing status and prestige as far as no longer being the only authorities on the subject of Yoga and/or its legitimate representatives. Ironically, the article itself points out that what the West has developed and called "Yoga" is actually neither what the ancients had in mind nor what authentic modern day Indian Yoga masters have in mind. The Yoga of the West is essentially an amalgam of some Yogic philosophy mixed with Western individuality, cynicism and hedonism. Further, the vast majority of Yoga practitioners in the West have nothing to do with Yoga philosophy and prefer to partake solely in the physical fitness aspects of the posture systems.[9]

It is therefore fitting that an Indian authority on the subject of Yoga should be included here. A world renowned spiritual teacher, and master of Indian Yoga, Vedanta Philosophy and Sanskrit of India, Swami Jyotirmayananda, had the following to say on the origins and universal practice of Yoga.

> "Yoga is a universal religion. It gives insight into every religion…Yoga embraces all religions of the world. It does not see the need of contradicting them. Its interest lies in giving a wider meaning to one's love for God. What is contradicted is limitation in understanding God, and a mental obstruction in developing love of God. All great mystics, saints and seers in all parts of the world proclaim the same reality, but, in different expressions, in different languages. Yogic principles are verified through all great personalities. Many practiced universal Yoga without giving it a Sanskrit name. The teachings of Jesus were inspired by the Yogic teachings that prevailed in antiquity through Buddhism. Socrates was inspired by Yogic wisdom. Directly or indirectly, all great personalities drink deep from the universal stream of wisdom which is Yoga…therefore Christianity is nothing but Yoga."
>
> —Swami Jyotirmayananda

The same sentiment, may be seen in a statement which appears in the book *Living Yoga*.[10] It is surprising to see the following statement by Mr. Georg Feuerstein in light of other statements which suggest that he advocates the idea that "Yoga" originated in India. Many advocates of the "out of India view" would like to present a universalistic perspective of Yoga philosophically or figuratively, but when it comes to discussing the origins they suddenly become fierce proponents of the idea that Yoga is a high philosophy originated by ancient Indian sages and that what other people have done through history is little more than primitive attempts at philosophy which have been influenced by contact with India.

> So, the metaphysical explanations of Yoga should not prove a stumbling block to anyone with a genuine desire to explore this ancient tradition. It is this built-in flexibility that has allowed the Yoga tradition to adapt itself so well to the conditions of the West. It can be as meaningful for nondogmatic agnostics, Christians, or Jews as it is for Hindus.
>
> Yoga, then, is a universal art, which flourishes wherever a person is dedicated to higher values, to a way of life that outdistances the egotistical preoccupations of the unenlightened mind: the way of inner joy and outer harmony.
>
> -Living Yoga by Georg Feuerstein, Stephan Bodian,
> with the staff of Yoga Journal

The Early Practice of Yoga in India and the Early Connection to Ancient Egypt[11]

One of a handful of depictions of a person in a Yoga posture being worshipped by two others and two serpents on either side. (Indus Valley-Pre Aryan)

In reference to the pictograph above as well as Yoga and its origins in the Indus tradition and the possibility of Yoga practices from outside India influencing the development of Yoga in India, the mythologist Joseph Campbell explained the following:

> "The basic treatise on Yoga is the *Yoga Sutras, Thread of Yoga,* a work attributed to an ancient saint whose name, Patanjali (from pata, "falling," plus anjali, "the joined hands"), is explained by a legend of his having dropped from heaven in the shape of a small snake into the hands of the grammarian Panini, just as the latter, was bringing his palms together in prayers.[12] Its date is under debate, some assigning it to the second century B.C., others to the fifth century A.D. or later;[13] all, however, recognizing that the ideas and disciplines represented are certainly older than this writing, some perhaps dating back even to the Indus civilization, ca. 2500-1500 B.C. For the earliest known evidences of Yoga appear on a half-dozen or so of the Indus Valley seals, an example of which appears here. (see above) Two attendant serpents elevate their giant forms behind a pair of worshipers kneeling at either hand of an enthroned figure seated in what appears to be a posture of Yoga. And the fact that the elevation of the so-called Serpent Power is one of the leading motifs of Yogic symbolism suggests that we may have here an explicit pictorial reference not only to the legend of some prehistoric Yogi, but also to the concept of the unfoldment through Yoga of this subtle spiritual force.
>
> If so, the question arises whether some sort of Yoga may not have been practiced outside India at that time as well. For a number of the symbols that are interpreted in psychological terms in Yogic lore appear also in the monuments of other ancient cultures-where, however, no explanatory texts such as those that can be studied from the Hindu-Buddhist sphere are known."[14]

This extremely important passage from the eminent scholar brings up several most significant and insightful points with far reaching implications. The motif of the serpent and the raising of the "Serpent Power" can indeed be found in almost every culture which has practiced the art that is popularly known as "Kundalini Yoga" or Serpent Power Yoga. However, in Ancient Egypt we see almost an exact reproduction (see below) of the scene from the Indus Valley (above) in the Serpent Power system of Ancient Egypt. That is not a common occurrence and therefore points to a more than casual connection between these two cultures. That is the difference in the relationship between India and Egypt that sets them apart from other countries. The sheer number and exactness of correlations, backed up by evidences of contact between the two cultures in ancient times strongly demonstrates a connection in which India adopted certain teachings, disciplines and iconographies that were not in India prior to the contact.

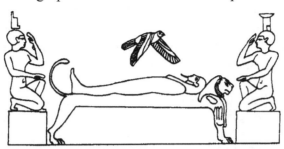

The God Asar (Osiris) with the goddess Aset (Isis) at the foot of the bed and goddess Nebethet (Nephthys) at the head.

The goddesses are known as the two sisters and as the *Arati,* serpents sisters. Thus, even the serpents are present in the image in a subtle way. Further, the Kamitan word "Arat" (𓆗), means goddess and the serpent sign is part of the names 𓎛𓆗 *Nebethet Arat* and 𓊃𓆗 *Aset Arat* of the two goddesses (see below). In the *Asarian Resurrection* Myth, one of the oldest myths of Ancient Egypt, we are informed that the goddess in her dual form, Aset and Nebethet, are the engineers of the resurrection of Asar. As we learn from the science of Kundalini Yoga as practiced in modern India, Kundalini is a goddess who manifests in a dual form, *Ida and Pingala.* They join and move up the subtle spine of the Aspirant (Yogi) and cause the raising of consciousness to cosmic levels as represented by the Chakras or psycho-spiritual energy centers. The point between the eyebrows (brow) signifies the attainment of dual vision (Cosmic consciousness {what the Indian Yoga systems refers to as *Jiva Mukti* or Buddhists Enlightenment} and phenomenal awareness). The seventh chakra signifies the attainment of transcendental consciousness. These teachings are compatible between Ancient Egypt and India. Along with this motif from Ancient Egypt, we can see not just the iconography of the Serpent Power, but also the *"technical specifications"* and *"facts"* related to the Kamitan Yoga practices and the *"concept of the unfoldment through Yoga of this subtle spiritual force."*

Goddesses Nebethet (left) and Aset (right) –with their serpent designations (goddess)

"The Goddess Uadjit cometh unto thee in the form of the living Uraeus, to anoint thy head with their flames. She riseth up on the left side of thy head, and she shineth from the right side of thy temples without speech; they rise up on thy head during each and every hour of the day, even as they do for their father Ra, and through them the terror which thou inspirest in the holy spirits is increased, and because Uadjit and Nekhebet rise up on thy head, and because thy brow becometh the portion of thy head whereon they establish themselves, even as they do upon the brow of Ra, and because they never leave thee, awe of thee striketh into the souls which are made perfect."

The preceding scripture from the Ancient Egyptian ceremonies is echoed in the *Pert M Heru* text of Ancient Egypt, *The Ancient Egyptian Book Enlightenment*. The state of enlightenment is further described in Chapters 83 and 85 where the initiate realizes that the seven Uraeus deities or bodies (immortal parts of the spirit) have been reconstituted:

"The seven Uraeuses are my body... my image is now eternal."

These seven Uraeuses are described as the *"seven souls of Ra"* and *"the seven arms of the balance (Maat)."* These designations of course refer to the seven spheres of the balance scales of Maat which correspond to the seven Chakras of the Indian Kundalini system.[15]

Below- Ancient Egyptian depiction of the god Asar with the two serpent goddesses in the form of a Caduceus, symbolizing the Serpent Power (Kundalini Yoga).

Plate 1: Below left-The Hindu god Shiva, "the Master Yogi," sitting in meditation on the tiger skin. This iconography is thought to be a late development of the "the Indus Yogi" (above)

Plate 2: Below right- an Ancient Egyptian man in the Lotus Posture[16]

In Kamitan Yogic mysticism, the "leonine bed" (feline motif) symbolizes the sleep of death from which the awakening of enlightenment will occur as the feline Life Force essence, termed *Sekhem* in Ancient Egypt, is cultivated. The avian motif symbolizes the rising of consciousness, metaphorically referred to as "resurrection." In Indian Yogic mysticism, the lotus posture on the bedding of the tiger (again a feline motif) skin has assumed the same role. Therefore, the feline motif is maintained throughout both the Kamitan and Indian systems and they are therefore compatible in class, gender, function and mythic metaphor.

The Ancient Egyptians Practiced Yoga

Most people in Western Culture have heard of Yoga as an exercise, however, Yoga is a vast science of human psychology and spiritual transformation which includes physical and mental health as the prerequisite for further progress into philosophical and meditative disciplines. Yoga, in all of its disciplines, was practiced in Ancient Egypt (Kamit, Kamut, Kamit or Ta-Meri) and is the subject of the Ancient Egyptian Mysteries. As in India, Yoga, as it was practiced in Ancient Egypt, included the disciplines of virtuous living, dietary purification, study of the wisdom teachings and their practice in daily life, psychophysical and psycho-spiritual exercises and meditation. Practitioners of Indian Yoga, Buddhist Yoga and Chinese Yoga (Taoism) today refer to all of these disciplines as Yogic disciplines. Therefore, the Ancient Egyptians were also practitioners of Yoga Philosophy. Through a process of gradually blending these disciplines in the course of ordinary life, an individual can effect miraculous changes in {{her/his}} life and thereby achieve the supreme goal of all existence, the goal of Yoga: Union with the Higher Self.

What is "Egyptian Yoga" and What is The Philosophy Behind It?

As previously discussed, Yoga in all of its forms was practiced in Egypt apparently earlier than anywhere else in our history. This point of view is supported by the fact that there is documented scriptural and iconographical evidence of the disciplines of virtuous living, dietary purification, study of the wisdom teachings and their practice in daily life, psychophysical and psycho-spiritual exercises and meditation being practiced in Ancient Egypt, long before the evidence of its existence is detected in India (including the Indus Valley Civilization) or any other early civilization (Sumer, Greece, China, etc.).

19

The teachings of Yoga are at the heart of *Prt m Hru*. As explained earlier, the word "Yoga" is a Sanskrit term meaning to unite the individual with the Cosmic. The term has been used in this volume for ease of communication since the word "Yoga" has received wide popularity, especially in Western countries in recent years. The Ancient Egyptian equivalent term to the Sanskrit word Yoga is: *"Sma, Sema or Smai."* The Kamitan language did not record vowels, so there is no way to know the exact spelling or pronunciation that would have been used. It could have been *Sma, Sema, Sama, or Soma.* We will use the terms *Sema* or *Smai* (the Ancient Egyptian terms) interchangeably throughout this text to refer to Kamitan Yoga. *Sema* or *Smai* mean union, and the following determinative terms give it a spiritual significance, at once equating it with the term "Yoga" as it is used in India. When used in conjunction with the Ancient Egyptian symbol which means land, *"Ta,"* the term "union of the two lands" arises.

Sema (or *Smai*) *Tawi* (*Taui*)
(From Chapter 4 of the *Prt m Hru*)

In Chapter 4[17] and Chapter 17[18] of the *Prt m Hru,* a term *"Sma, Sema or Smai* Tawi" is used. It means "Union of the two lands of Egypt," ergo "Egyptian Yoga." The two lands refer to the two main districts of the country (North and South). In ancient times, Egypt was divided into two sections or land areas. These were known as Lower and Upper Egypt. In Ancient Egyptian mystical philosophy, the land of Upper Egypt relates to the divinity Heru (Horus), who represents the Higher Self, and the land of Lower Egypt relates to Set, the divinity of the lower self. So *Sema* (*Smai*) *Taui* means "the union of the two lands" or the "Union of the lower self with the Higher Self. The lower self relates to that which is negative and uncontrolled in the human mind including worldliness, egoism, ignorance, etc. (Set), while the Higher Self relates to that which is above temptations and is good in the human heart as well as in touch with Transcendental consciousness (Heru). Thus, we also have the Ancient Egyptian term *Sema* (*Smai*) *Heru-Set,* or the union of Heru and Set. So Sema (Smai) Taui or Sema (Smai) Heru-Set are the Ancient Egyptian words which are to be translated as "Egyptian Yoga."

Above: the main symbol of Egyptian Yoga: *Sma.* The Ancient Egyptian language and symbols provide the first "historical" record of Yoga Philosophy and Religious literature. The hieroglyph Sma, ⚲ "Sema," represented by the union of two lungs and the trachea, symbolizes that the union of the duality, that is, the Higher Self and lower self, leads to Non-duality, the One, singular consciousness.

More Ancient Egyptian Symbols of Yoga

(†)

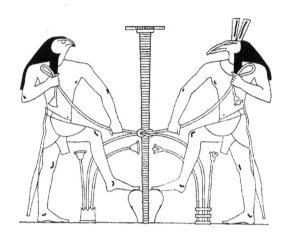

Above: Sema (Smai) Heru-Set,

Heru and Set join forces to tie up the symbol of Union (Sema or Sma). The Sema symbol refers to the Union of Upper Egypt (Lotus) and Lower Egypt (Papyrus) under one ruler, but also at a more subtle level, it refers to the union of one's Higher Self and lower self (Heru and Set), as well as the control of one's breath (Life Force) through the union (control) of the lungs (breathing organs). The character of Heru and Set are an integral part of the *Pert Em Heru.*

The central and most popular character within Ancient Egyptian Religion of Asar is Heru, who is an incarnation of his father, Asar. Asar was killed by his brother Set who, out of greed and demoniac (Setian) tendency, craved to be the ruler of Egypt. With the help of Djehuti, the God of purified intellect, Aset, the great mother of intuitional wisdom and Hetheru, his consort and goddess of sublimated sexual energy, Heru prevailed in the battle against Set for the rulership of Kamit (Egypt). Heru's struggle symbolizes the struggle of every human being to regain rulership of the Higher Self and to subdue the lower self.

The most ancient writings in our historical period are from the Ancient Egyptians. These writings are referred to as hieroglyphics. The original name given to these writings by the Ancient Egyptians is *Medu Neter,* meaning "the writing of God" or *Neter Medu* or "Divine Speech." These writings were inscribed in temples, coffins and papyruses and contained the teachings in reference to the spiritual nature of the human being and the ways to promote spiritual emancipation, awakening or resurrection. The Ancient Egyptian proverbs presented in this text are translations from the original hieroglyphic scriptures. An example of hieroglyphic text was presented above in the form of the text of Sema (Smai) Taui or "Egyptian Yoga."

Egyptian Philosophy may be summed up in the following proverbs, which clearly state that the soul is heavenly or divine and that the human being must awaken to the true reality, which is the Spirit, Self.

"Self knowledge is the basis of true knowledge."

The African Origins of Hatha Yoga

"Soul to heaven, body to earth."

"Man is to become God-like through a life of virtue and the cultivation of the spirit through scientific knowledge, practice and bodily discipline."

"Salvation is accomplished through the efforts of the individual. There is no mediator between man and {{his/her}} salvation."

"Salvation is the freeing of the soul from its bodily fetters, becoming a God through knowledge and wisdom, controlling the forces of the cosmos instead of being a slave to them, subduing the lower nature and through awakening the Higher Self, ending the cycle of rebirth and dwelling with the Neters who direct and control the Great Plan."

What is Hatha Yoga?

The following information was taken from Wikipedia Encyclopedia, which quotes, one of the most respected Western scholars of Yoga and Indian Spirituality.

> **Hatha yoga** is also known as Hatha vidya. It is a particular system of Yoga introduced by Yogi Swatmarama, a yogic sage of the 15th century in India, and compiler of the Hatha Yoga Pradipika. Hatha Yoga is derived from the *Hinayana* (narrow path) and *Mahayana* (great path) traditions of Buddhism, as well as the *Sahajayana* (spontaneous path) and *Vajrayana* (concerning matters of sexuality) traditions of Tantra. The Hatha Yoga of Swatmarama and his contemporaries differs from the Raja Yoga of Patanjali in that it focuses on *shatkarma*, the purification of the physical as leading to the purification of the mind (*ha*) and *prana*, or vital energy (*tha*). The Raja Yoga posited by Patanjali begins with a purification of the mind (*yamas*) and spirit (*niyamas*), then comes to the body via *asana* (body postures) and *pranayama* (breath). Hatha Yoga is what most people associate with the word "Yoga" and is mainly practiced for mental, physical health, and vitality outside of India.[19]

The term "Hatha Yoga" is an Indian idiom. In Ancient Egypt the practice of physical postures for the purpose of attaining spiritual enlightenment was called "Sema Paut" or union (Sema) with the Gods and Goddesses. As stated earlier, the term "Hatha Yoga" means Forceful Yoga". Specifically, it means yoga, that is, the movement of union of the lower self with the higher, that is artificially enhanced through certain postures. However, the practice of Yoga, as it developed in India (+1,000 B.C.E.-200 B.C.E.), was eventually classified as a science with eight steps. So the "posture", in that system of Yoga, was and continues to be seen as a help to the other seven disciplines. The concept of "posture" was introduced by the Indian sage Patanjali in 200 B.C.E. However, his system of Yoga only mentioned posture for sitting to meditate and not the concept of a sequence of postures as known today as "Hatha Yoga." The Yoga system of Patanjali includes eight practices and the sitting practice is only one eighth of the practice. The complete program is included below.

1- <u>Self control (yama):</u> Non- violence, truthfulness, chastity, avoidance of greed.

2- <u>Practice of virtues (niyama):</u> Actions to avoid in order to maintain yama.

3- <u>Postures (asana):</u> To condition the body and prepare the mind and body for meditation.

4- <u>Breath control (pranayama):</u> Controlling the breath is controlling the Life Force; controlling the Life Force is controlling the mind.

5- <u>Restraint (pratyahara):</u> Disciplining the sense organs to avoid overindulgence and physical temptation of the body: food, sex, drugs, etc.

6- <u>Steadying the mind (dharana):</u> Practice focusing the mind. Concentrating the mental rays on one subject over a short period of time.

23

7- <u>Meditation (dhyana):</u> When the object of concentration engulfs the entire mind and concentration continues spontaneously.

8- <u>Deep meditation (samadhi):</u> Personality dissolves temporarily into the object of meditation, experience of super-consciousness.

In the Yoga Sutras of Sage Patanjali (c. 200 B.C.E.), the following instruction is given for the practitioner of Yoga:

योगश्चित्तवृत्तिनिरोधः

YOGASH CHITTA VRITTI NIRODHAH.
Sutra 2: Yoga is the intentional stopping of the mind-stuff (thought waves).

This is desirable because:

वृत्तिसारूप्यमितरत्र

VRITTI SARUPYAM ITARATRA.
Sutra 4: "At times when the mind stuff flows indiscriminately, "the seer" becomes "identified" with the thought-waves."

Patanjali went on to say that due to the identification of the seer (our true self) with the thoughts, we believe ourselves to be mortal and limited instead of immortal and immutable. He further says that there is no need to worry because through the steady practice of Yoga (dispassion, devotion, mind control exercises of meditation), even the most unruly mind can be controlled. Thus, the individual will discover their true self when the ***"Chitta"*** (thought waves) are controlled. It is as if one looks at oneself through colored sunglasses and believes oneself to be that color. In the same way, Yoga is the process of uncovering the eyes from the illusion of the mind's thought waves.

Nevertheless, regardless of whether Yoga originated in India or in Ancient Egypt (Africa), a question that will be explored later, it is certain that the Yoga Postures are special exercises which engender a psycho-physical and psycho-spiritual transformation which leads to harmony of the mind, body and spirit. Throughout history, the teachings of Yoga have been associated with religion and mythology. In order to understand the deep psycho-spiritual symbolism of each posture in the Ancient Egyptian tradition, it is be necessary to understand the creation myth of ancient Egypt and the Myth of Asar (Osiris). These teachings impart profound wisdom on the understanding of the soul, creation, and the journey of every human being through life.

Where is the land of Egypt?

A map of North East Africa showing the location of the land of *Ta-Meri* or *Kamut,* also known as Ancient Egypt.

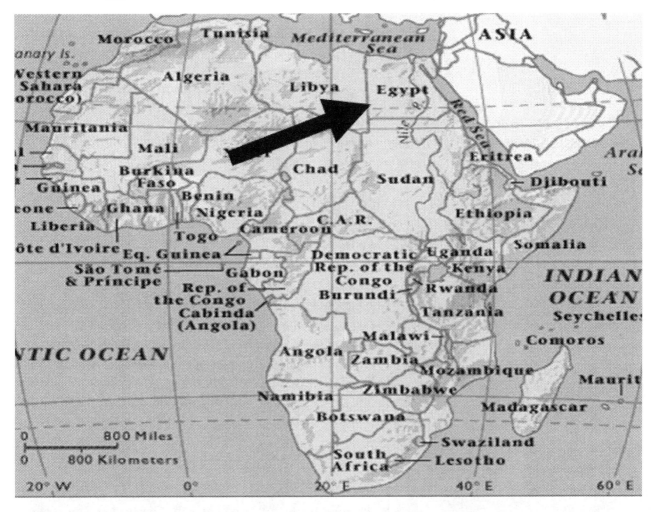

The Ancient Egyptians lived for thousands of years in the northeastern corner of the African continent in the area known as the Nile River Valley. The Nile River was a source of dependable enrichment for the land and allowed them to prosper for a very long time. Their prosperity was so great that they created art, culture, religion, philosophy and a civilization which has not been duplicated ever since. The Ancient Kamitans (Egyptians) based their government and business concerns on spiritual values and therefore, enjoyed an orderly society which included equality between the sexes, and a legal system based on universal spiritual laws.

The *Egyptian Mystery System* is a tribute to their history, culture and legacy. As historical insights unfold, it becomes clearer that modern culture has derived its basis from Ancient Egypt, though the credit is not often given, nor the integrity of the practices maintained in the new religions. This is another important reason to study Ancient Egyptian Philosophy, to discover the principles which allowed their civilization to prosper over a period of thousands of years in order to bring our systems of government, religion and social structures to a harmony with ourselves, humanity and with nature.

The flow of the Nile brought annual floods to the Nile Valley and this provided irrigation and new soil nutrients every year that allowed for regular crops when worked on time. This regularity and balance of nature inspired the population to adopt a culture of order and duty based on cosmic order: Maat. This idea extends to the understanding of Divine justice and reciprocity. So if work is performed on time and in cooperation with nature, there will be order, balance and peace as well as prosperity in life.

Kamit (Egypt) is located in the north-eastern corner of the continent of Africa. It is composed of towns along the banks of the Hapi (Nile River). In the north there is the Nile Delta region where the river contacts the Mediterranean Sea. This part is referred to as the North or Lower Egypt, "lower," because that is the lowest elevation and the river flows from south to north. The middle of the country is referred to as Middle Egypt. The south is referred to as Upper Egypt because it is the higher elevation and the river flows from there to the north. The south is the older region of the dynastic civilization and the middle and north are later.

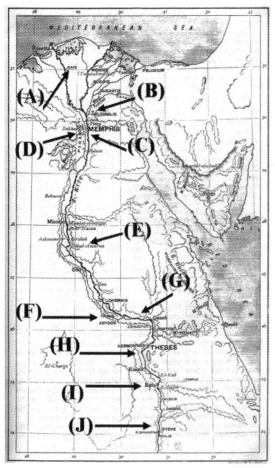

The Ancient Egyptian cities were related to certain divinities and their respective religious theologies.

The Land of Ancient Egypt-Nile Valley - The cities wherein the theology of the Trinity of Amun-Ra-Ptah was developed were: A- Sais (temple of Net), B- Anu (Heliopolis- temple of Ra), C-Men-nefer or Hetkaptah (Memphis, temple of Ptah), and D- Sakkara (Pyramid Texts), E- Akhet-Aton (City of Akhnaton, temple of Aton), F- Abdu (temple of Asar)-Greek Abydos, G- Denderah (temple of Hetheru), H- Waset (Thebes, temple of Amun), I- Edfu (temple of Heru), J- Philae (temple of Aset). The cities wherein the theology of the Trinity of Asar-Aset-Heru was developed were Anu, Abdu, Philae, Denderah and Edfu.

The Sphinx and its contemporary architecture throughout Kamit give us the earliest history, the earliest recorded evidence of the practice of advanced religion anywhere in the world. The Sphinx has now been proven to be the earliest example of the practice of religion in human history, 10,000 BCE.

The next religion appears in India at about 2,500 to 3,000 BCE. We have shown in the book *African Origins* that there was a direct relationship between the Indians and the Ancient Egyptians/Ancient Africans, so much so that the basic tenants of Hinduism and Buddhism can be directly correlated to Shetaut Neter.

When Was Ancient Egyptian Civilization in Existence?

KAMIT

(Ancient Egypt)

A Brief History of Ancient Egypt

Christianity was partly an outgrowth of Judaism, which was itself an outgrowth of Ancient Egyptian culture and religion. So who were the Ancient Egyptians? From the time that the early Greek philosophers set foot on African soil to study the teachings of mystical spirituality in Egypt (900-300 B.C.E.), Western society and culture was forever changed. Ancient Egypt had such a profound effect on Western civilization as well as on the native population of Ancient India (Dravidians) that it is important to understand the history and culture of Ancient Egypt, and the nature of its spiritual tradition in more detail.

The history of Egypt begins in the far reaches of history. It includes The Dynastic Period, The Hellenistic Period, Roman and Byzantine Rule (30 B.C.E.-638 A.C.E.), the Caliphate and the Mamalukes (642-1517 A.C.E.), Ottoman Domination (1082-1882 A.C.E.), British colonialism (1882-1952 A.C.E.), as well as modern, Arab-Islamic Egypt (1952- present).

Ancient Egypt or Kamit, was a civilization that flourished in Northeast Africa along the Nile River from before 5,500 B.C.E. until 30 B.C.E. In 30 B.C.E., Octavian, who was later known as the Roman Emperor, Augustus, put the last Egyptian King, Ptolemy XIV, a Greek ruler, to death. After this Egypt was formally annexed to Rome. Egyptologists normally divide Ancient Egyptian history into the following periods: The Early Dynastic Period; The Old Kingdom or Old Empire; The First Intermediate Period; The Middle Kingdom or Middle Empire; The Second Intermediate Period; The New Kingdom or New Empire (1,532-1,070 B.C.E.); The third Intermediate Period (1,070-712 B.C.E.); The Late Period (712-332 B.C.E.).

In the Late Period the following groups controlled Egypt. The Nubian Dynasty (712-657 B.C.E.); The Persian Dynasty (525-404 B.C.E.); The Native Revolt and re-establishment of Egyptian rule by Egyptians (404-343 B.C.E.); The Second Persian Period (343-332 B.C.E.); The Ptolemaic or Greek Period (332 B.C.E.- c. 30 B.C.E.); Roman Period (c.30 B.C.E.-395 A.C.E.); The Byzantine Period (395-640 A.C.E) and The Arab Conquest Period (640 A.C.E.-present). The individual dynasties are numbered, generally in Roman numerals, from I through XXX. However, the realization of the geological evidence of the Great Sphinx and the discovery of the new Dynasty previously unknown to the Egyptologists, the history needs to be revised. See the full revision in the book African Origins of Civilization by Muata Ashby (2002).

The period after the New Kingdom saw greatness in culture and architecture under the rulership of Ramses II. However, after his rule, Egypt saw a decline from which it would never recover. This is the period of the downfall of Ancient Egyptian culture in which the Libyans ruled after the Tanite (XXI) Dynasty. This was followed by the Nubian conquerors who founded the XXII Dynasty and tried to restore Egypt to her past glory. However, having been weakened by the social and political turmoil of wars, Ancient Egypt fell to the Persians once more. The Persians conquered the country until the Greeks, under Alexander, conquered them. The Romans followed the Greeks, and finally the Arabs conquered the land of Egypt in 640 A.C.E to the present.

However, the history which has been classified above is only the history of the "Dynastic Period." It reflects the view of traditional Egyptologists who have refused to accept the evidence of a Predynastic period in Ancient Egyptian history contained in Ancient Egyptian documents such as the *Palermo Stone, Royal Tablets at Abydos, Royal Papyrus of Turin,* the *Dynastic List* of *Manetho,* and the eye-witness accounts of Greek historians Herodotus (c. 484-425 B.C.E.) and Diodorus. These sources speak clearly of a Pre-dynastic society which stretches far into antiquity. The Dynastic Period is what most people think of whenever Ancient Egypt is mentioned. This period is when the pharaohs (kings) ruled. The latter part of the Dynastic Period is when the Biblical story of Moses, Joseph, Abraham, etc., occurs (c. 2100? -1,000? B.C.E). Therefore, those with a Christian background generally only have an idea about Ancient Egypt as it is related in the Bible. The tradition based on the old Jewish bible recounting about how the Jews were used for forced labor and the construction of the great monuments of Egypt such as the Great Pyramids is impossible since these were created in the predynastic age, thousands of years before Abraham, the supposed first Jew, ever existed. Although this biblical notion is very limited in scope, the significant impact of Ancient Egypt on Hebrew and Christian culture is evident even from the biblical scriptures. Actually, Egypt existed much earlier than most traditional Egyptologists are prepared to admit. The new archeological evidence related to the great Sphinx monument on the Giza Plateau and the ancient writings by Manetho, one of the last High Priests of Ancient Egypt, show that Ancient Egyptian history begins earlier than 10,000 B.C.E. and may date back to as early as 30,000-50,000 B.C.E.

Evidence of Contact Between Ancient Egypt and India

Where is India and What is its Physical Proximity to Kamit {Egypt}?

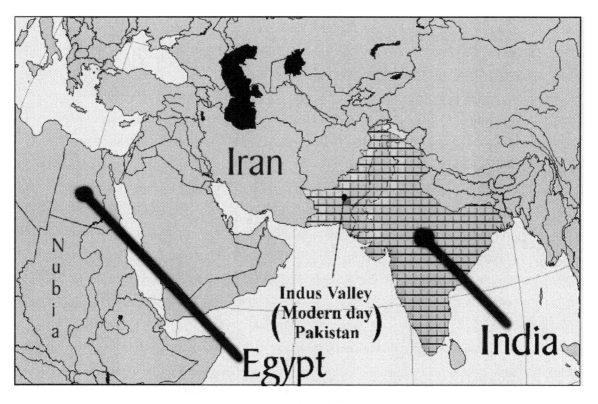

Above: Map of Southern Asia and Eastern Africa

The Ethiopian Kush or Cush refers to the kingdom of Nubia[20], which according to the ancient writings of Egypt as well as the writings of the classical Greek historians is the source of both Ancient Egyptian civilization as well as Indian civilization.

The following are statements from the writings of Greek classical writers who traveled the ancient world and reported about the peoples they saw and the lands where they lived as well as their interrelationships.

"I shall speak of the king who reigned next, whose name was Sesostris[i] He, the priests said, first of all proceeded in a fleet of ships of war from the Arabian gulf along the shores of the Indian ocean, subduing the nations as he went, until he finally reached a sea which could not be navigated by reason of the shoals. **Hence he returned to Egypt, where, they told me, he collected a vast armament, and made a progress by land across the continent, conquering every people which fell in his way.**

   In this way he traversed the whole continent of Asia, whence he passed on into Europe, and made himself master of Scythia and of Thrace, beyond which countries I do not think that his army extended its march."

- History of Herodotus (Greek historian 484 B.C.E.)

"All the Indian tribes I mentioned ... their skins are all of the same color, much like the Ethiopians."

-History of Herodotus (Greek historian 484 B.C.E.)

"And upon his return to Greece, they gathered around and asked, "tell us about this great land of the Blacks called Ethiopia." And Herodotus said, **"There are two great Ethiopian nations, one in Sind (India) and the other in Egypt."**

-Diodorus (Greek historian 100 B.C.)

"From Ethiopia, he (Osiris {Asar})[ii] passed through Arabia, bordering upon the Red Sea to as far as India, and the remotest inhabited coasts; he built likewise many cities in India, one of which he called Nysa, willing to have remembrance of that (Nysa) in Egypt where he was brought up. At this Nysa in India he planted Ivy, which continues to grow there, but nowhere else in India or around it. **He left likewise many other marks of his being in those parts, by which the latter inhabitants are induced, and do affirm, that this God was born in India.** He likewise addicted himself to the hunting of elephants, and took care to have statues of himself in every place, as lasting monuments of his expedition."

- Diodorus (Greek historian 100 B.C.)
[i] Senusert I, reigned in 1,971. B.C.E.
[ii] Reigned c. 10,000 B.C.E.

Some modern day Hindus continue to believe Egypt is their ancestral home.

-

"Some Hindus claim the Nile to be one of their sacred rivers; they also regard as sacred the Mountains of the Moon (in Uganda-Congo) and Mount Meru (in Tanzania). Both in India and in the Indianized Kingdoms, Southern Mount Meru was regarded as the mythical dwelling place of the Gods. Each of these statements reflect millennia old relationships between the blacks of Africa and South Asia. The Ethiopian Kebra Negast regarded Western India as a portion of the Ethiopian Empire. **"Murugan, the God of mountains", the son of the mother Goddess is a prominent and typical deity of the Dravidian India.** It is interesting to note that at least 25 tribes in East Africa worship "Murungu" as supreme God, and like the Dravidian God Murugan, the African Murungu resides in sacred mountains."

-From: U.P. Upadhyaya
"Dravidian and Negro-African International Journal of Dravidian Linguistics"
v.5,No 1 January 1976, p 39.

Indian Archeologists Discover Contact and Correlations Between Ancient Egypt and India

What follows is a portion of the research contributed by Indian scholars based on archeological excavations, working in India and Egypt on the question of contact and interaction between Ancient Egypt and India. The maritime trade between Ancient Egypt and India is known to have lasted longer and to have been more reliable than the over-land route through Asia Minor (Afghanistan, Iran, Iraq and Syria.). Therefore, during the periods when Egyptian rule over Asia Minor waned, due to wars and the influx of Indo-European peoples from the North of Asia, the contact between Ancient Egypt and India was maintained by sea.

"Direct contact between the two countries (India and Egypt) during this period (Pharaonic Egypt 3400-525 B.C.) is suggested by some highly specialized artifacts which are found in India as well as in Egypt but which, surprisingly, are absent in the vast West Asian region between-Afghanistan, Iran, Iraq and Syria."[21]

The material evidence of such contact includes:

"HEAD-RESTS: Indian head-rests found at some Neolithic sites such as T. Narsipur, Hemmige, and Hallur-all in Karnataka in south India-may be consigned to dates in the first half of the second millennium B.C. on the basis of radio-carbon tests. Curiously, they occur only in south India[22] and have no parallels elsewhere in tile subcontinent except for a solitary contemporaneous specimen from Chanudaro assigned to Jhukar levels[23] of circa 1800 B.C.

In Egypt, similar head-rests belonging to a period spanning the pre-Dynasty Period to Roman times have been discovered. A number of them are made of wood but in some, intended for royalty and the aristocracy, costlier materials such as ivory and lapis lazuli are employed. Egyptian headrests occur in a variety of forms. Incidentally, certain tribes of Africa[24] and India use wooden head-rests even today.[25] Strikingly identical head-rests have also been carved in rock bruisings at Piklilial in Karnataka (India), which site has, interestingly also yielded specimens in pottery belonging to the Neolithic period."

Plate above: Picture of a display at the Brooklyn Museum (1999-2000) showing the similarity between the headrest of Ancient Egypt (foreground) and those used in other parts of Africa (background). (Photo by M. Ashby)

It has been demonstrated, through late 20th century photographic surveys, that the peoples of certain areas in South India dress and appear indistinguishable from African peoples in terms of ethnic traits such as their hair, skin tone and physiognomy.[26] Again, this confirms the eye-witness accounts of Herodotus, who noted the similitude in the physical appearance of the Ancient Egyptians, Ethiopians and Indians.

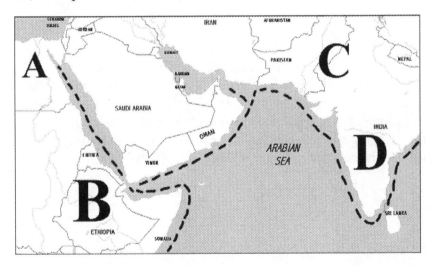

The Maritime Trade Rout Between Ancient Egypt (A) and the Indus (C).

Figure: Above-North-east Africa, Asia Minor, South Asia (India) and the Egyptian-Indian trade routes in the Hellenistic (Greek) and Roman times.[27]

It is sometimes not realized how important trade routes and commerce can be to a civilization. In Ancient times the Indus Valley civilization as well as Ancient Egyptian civilization relied upon trade in order to sustain the economic prosperity of the nation. This was especially true in the time before the concept of currency and monetary exchange was invented. This view is supported by most scholars, one example is *S. M El Mansouri*, as he writes:

> "We cannot ignore the influence that trade has upon the relationship between nations. It carries the culture of one country to another. Ideas, philosophy and religions are transferred from nation to nation through trade, handicrafts, books, and artistic products go from people to people along trade routes.
>
> In many periods, India had direct relations with Egypt, Syria, and other parts of the Hellenistic West. Kings, as well as independent cities, depended to a large extent on the tributes paid by the peasantry, but a considerable portion of Egyptian - and Indian revenues came from trade in olden times.
>
> There was a considerable body of foreign residents in the ports whose affairs were looked after by a special board of municipal commissioners. These foreigners could not all, of course, have been diplomats. Some of them were, in all probability, traders.
>
> When art flourishes (this means always good relationships) it is always connected with peace, religions, traditions, and philosophy."[28]

One only has to consider how true this is in modern times with a few examples, consider the impact of Western Culture on Japan, whose government and social structure was changed by the United States of America after World War Two. The United States of America itself has been influenced by Japanese business methods as well as the infusion of Buddhism, Yoga, Henna hand art, etc., from other countries with which it trades. In fact many countries feel overwhelmed by the culture of the United States of America and have taken measures to curtail its effects on their society (Ex. China, Iran). In reference to the maritime trade in the New Kingdom Period of Ancient Egypt, Professor D. A. Mackenzie writes in his book *"Egyptian Myth and Legend"*:

> "At the time of the XVIII dynasty, the boats of the Imperial Egyptians were plying on the Mediterranean and the Indian Oceans, and far distant countries which may never have heard of Egypt, were being subjected to cultural influences that had emanated from the Nile Valley."

The obvious cultural connection between Ancient Egypt and India led to several aspects of cultural interaction so it is no surprise to find many artifacts, concepts of philosophy and other factors that can be directly correlated. These factors of correlation solidify our understanding of early Indian culture as a development of or strongly influenced by Ancient Egyptian-African culture and civilization. That allows us to have a deeper understanding of the Indian practices and a better understanding of their original intent. One of the most important and fundamental items of correlation is the concept and symbol known as "OM".

The terms "Hari" and "Om" in Ancient Egypt and India

While *Om* is most commonly known as a *Sanskrit* mantra (word of power from India), it also appears in the Ancient Egyptian texts and is closely related to the Kamitan *Amun* in sound and Amen of Christianity. More importantly, it has the same meaning as Amun and is therefore completely compatible with the energy pattern of the entire group. According to the Egyptian Leyden papyrus, the name of the "Hidden God," referring to Amun, may be pronounced as *Om,* or *Am*.

Below you will find the ancient glyphs of the ancient Egyptian OM symbol. Note the similarity to the Indian symbol that follows.

"OM" from the Ancient Egyptian Leyden Papyrus

The ancient African text containing the OM is found in the Leyden Magical Papyrus in which Supreme Being is described as follows:

> "Great is thy name, Heir is thy name, Excellent is thy name, Hidden is thy name,. Mighty one of the gods and goddesses is thy name, "He whose name is hidden from all the gods and goddesses is thy name, OM (⊰⊱), Mighty Am is thy name; All the gods and goddesses is thy name…"

We know that OM is the name of Amun because of the epithet "Hidden" and OM is the nameless Ancient divinity because of the epithet "name is hidden". OM is also the ancient divinity Neberdjer (All encompassing Divinity) because of the epithet "All the gods and goddesses" so OM is the name given to the most ancient divinities of Kamit (Egypt) dating to the predynastic era (prior to 5000 BCE).

Om is a powerful sound; it represents the primordial sound of creation. Thus it appears in Ancient Egypt as Om or Am, in modern day India as Om, and in Christianity as Amen, being derived from Amun. Om may also be used for engendering mental calm prior to beginning recitation of a longer set of words of power or it may be used alone as described above. One Indian Tantric scripture (*Tattva Prakash*) states that Om or AUM can be used to achieve the mental state free of physical identification and can bring union with *Brahman* (the Absolute transcendental Supreme Being - God) if it is repeated 300,000 times. In this sense, mantras such as Om, Soham, Sivoham, Aham Brahmasmi are called *Moksha Mantras* or mantras which lead to union with the Absolute Self. Their shortness promotes greater concentration and force toward the primordial level of consciousness.

The Indian Sanskrit Symbol "Aum" or "Om"

There is one more important divine name which is common to both Indian as well as Ancient Egyptian mystical philosophy. The Sanskrit mantra *Hari Om* is composed of Om preceded by the word Hari. In Hinduism, *Hari* means: "He who is Tawny." The definition of tawny is: "A light golden brown." However, Vishnu is oftentimes represented as "blue-black." This is a reference to the dark colored skin of Vishnu and Krishna. Vishnu is usually depicted with a deep blue and Krishna is depicted with a deep blue or black hue symbolizing infinity and transcendence. Hari is one of Krishna's or Vishnu's many divine names.

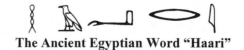

The Ancient Egyptian Word "Haari"

In the Ancient Egyptian mystical texts used to promote spiritual development (Words of Power or Heka - mantras), the word Haari also appears as one of the divine names[29] of God. Thus, the hekau-mantra Hari Om was also known and used in Ancient Egypt and constitutes a most powerful formula for mystical spiritual practice. Om or Am in Ancient Egypt was a shortened version of Amun, the divinity who like Vishnu and Krishna is depicted in Black or Blue (tawny). "Amun" also means hidden consciousness.

Amun (Hidden essence of creation-witnessing consciousness)

ANCIENT EGYPTIAN ORIGINS OF THE YOGA POSTURES

Recognition of "Egyptian" Yoga by Indian practitioners.

On the whole, recognition by Indian practitioners of the practice of special physical postures for the purpose of attaining enlightenment has been limited. However, one practitioner and disciple of one of India's most famous Hindu sages devoted a large portion of her book to acknowledging the Ancient Egyptian practice. In her book, HATHA YOGA: The Secret Language, Swami Sivananda Radha, the famous disciple of the Indian Guru Swami Sivananda, acknowledged the practice of yoga postures in Ancient Egypt and included in her book several [over a dozen] illustrations of the Egyptian postures.

History Of The Yogic Postures in Ancient Egypt and India

Since their introduction to the West the exercise system of India known as "Hatha Yoga" has gained much popularity. The disciplines related to the yogic postures and movements were developed in India around the 10th century A.C.E. by a sage named Goraksha.* Up to this time, the main practice was simply to adopt the cross-legged meditation posture known as the lotus for the purpose of practicing meditation. The most popular manual on Hatha Yoga is the ***Hatha-Yoga-Pradipika ("Light on the Forceful Yoga)***. It was authored by Svatmarama Yogin in mid. 14th century C.E.**

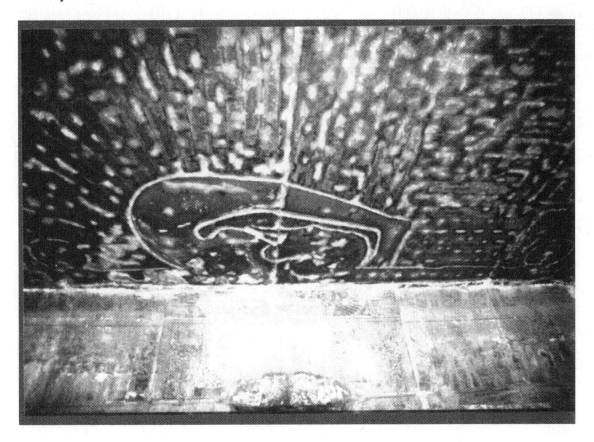

Plate 1: Above- The god Geb in the plough posture engraved on the ceiling of the antechamber to the Asarian Resurrection room of the Temple of Hetheru in Egypt. (photo taken by Ashby)

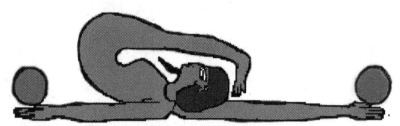

Prior to the emergence of the discipline the physical movements in India just before 1000 A.C.E., a series of virtually identical postures to those which were practiced in India can be found in various Ancient Egyptian papyruses and inscribed on the walls and ceilings of the temples. The Ancient Egyptian practice can be dated from 300 B.C.E 1,580 B.C.E and earlier. Exp. Temple of Hetheru (800-300 B.C.E.), Temple of Heru (800-300 B.C.E.), Tomb of Queen Nefertari (reigned 1,279-1,212 BC), Temple of Horemakhet (10,000 B.C.E.) and various other temples and papyruses from the New Kingdom Era 1,580 B.C.E). In Ancient Egypt the practice of the postures (called *Sema Paut* (Union with the gods and goddesses) or *Tjef Sema Paut Neteru* (movements to promote union with the gods and goddesses) were part of the ritual aspect of the spiritual myth which when practiced serve to harmonize the energies and promote the physical health of the body and direct the mind, in a meditative capacity, to discover and cultivate divine consciousness. These disciplines are part of a larger process called Sema or *Smai Tawi* (Egyptian Yoga). By acting and moving like the gods and goddesses one can essentially discover their character, energy and divine agency within one's consciousness and thereby also become one of their retinue, i.e. one with the Divine Self. In modern times, most practitioners of Hatha Yoga see it as a means to attain physical health only. However, even the practice in India had a mythic component which is today largely ignored.

(Below) In the upper right hand corner of the ceiling of the Peristyle Hall in the Temple of Aset a special image of the goddess Nut and the God Geb and the higher planes of existence can be seen. Nut and Geb. Below: -line drawing of the same scene. (Temple of Aset {Isis}).

The figure at left depicts another conceptualization of the Netherworld, which is at the same time the body of Nut in a forward bend posture.

The god Geb is on the ground practicing the Plough Yoga exercise posture. The goddess in the center symbolizes the lower heaven in which the moon traverses, the astral realm. The outermost goddess symbolizes the course of the sun in its astral journey and the causal plane.

Notice the characteristic Nubian headdress of Nut, which is also visible in the iconography of Bas. This iconography links the late Kamitan religion with that of the Pre-Dynastic era, and with the Nubian origins of Kamitan culture. Geb, who is in the plough posture, symbolizes the physical plane and all solid matter, while the goddesses represent the subtler levels of existence.

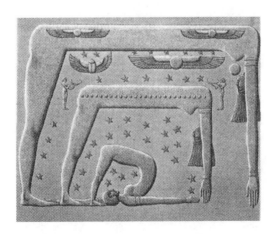

Records of <u>meditation as a discipline for lay people, as opposed to priests only</u>, first show up about 500 B.C. in both India and China. Contrary to what many Yoga students believe, his (Patanjali) text said little about Hatha Yoga postures, which weren't a widespread practice at the time. It only speaks of a sitting posture for the practice of meditation and nothing more.

Below: **Patanjali Yoga Sutras Sadhana Pad (200 B.C.E) - sutra 46: Asana – Trans. Swamiji Jyotirmayananda**:

Samadhi Pad Sutra 46: *seated pose for meditation*

Sutra 46

स्थिरसुखमासनम्

STHIRA SUKHAM ASANAM.

STHIRA: Steady. SUKHAM: Comfortable. ASANAM: Pose (for meditation).

Meaning

A seated pose (for meditation) that is steady and comfortable is called *Asana*.

Explanation

To attain success in the practice of concentration, meditation and *Samadhi*, an aspirant begins by developing steadiness of a meditative pose.

Samadhi Pad Sutra 48-49: *perfecting the seated pose for meditation*, as itself states, provided information on perfecting the "seated" pose and not a series of yoga postures as Hatha Yoga is known for today.

Plate: The Egyptian Gods and Goddesses act out the Creation through their movements (forward bend (Nut), spinal twist (Geb), journey of Ra and the squatting, standing motion (Shu and Nun).

Above: The varied postures found in the Kemetic papyruses and temple inscriptions. (Egyptian Yoga Postures Poster)

Below- the Goddess Parvati from India, practicing the tree Pose – modern rendition.

While the practice of the Tjef Neteru [Ancient Egyptian pyoga postures] was associated with the gods and goddesses from ancient times [before 2,000 B.C.E.0 Only at about the year 1,700 A.C.E. did the Shiva Samhita text Associate Hatha Yoga With the god and goddess Shiva and Parvati (Shakti)

The origins of Hatha Yoga have been associated with Tantric Buddhism and not in Hinduism since we find evidence of its early practice by Tantric Buddhists and rejection of Hatha Yoga by the Hindu sages. Hatha Yoga is clearly rejected in the Laghu -Yoga - Vasishtha (5.6.86, 92), an early text of Yoga philosophy, which maintains that it merely leads to pain. Some of the criticisms against Hatha Yoga were especially against the magical undercurrents of the practice. Tantric Buddhism gave rise to the earliest practice of certain postures in India as a means to enhance spiritual evolution. Before this time, the only reference to Asana or posture was the sitting posture for meditation, mentioned in the Raja Yoga Sutras by Patanjali. In ancient Kamit there were at least 24 postures in the spiritual practice prior to the time of Patanjali. In the practice of Kamitan *Tjef Neteru* (Egyptian Hatha Yoga, the "magic"[30] consists in using postures to engender certain alignments with spiritual energies and cosmic forces. This is the kind of practice repudiated by the Hindu sages but adopted by the Tantric Buddhists. Between the years 100 A.C.E. and 1000 A.C.E. the Buddhist Kaula school developed some postures. Then Goraksha developed what is regarded by present day Hatha Yoga practitioners as a practice similar to the present day. However, the number of postures only reached 15 at the time of the Hatha Yoga Pradipika scripture. The Mysore family was instrumental in the development since they were strong patrons of Hatha Yoga. Subsequent teachers developed more postures and vinyasa[31] (practice of postures in set sequence-which was not practiced in early Indian Hatha Yoga) up to the 20th century where there are over 200. The teacher Krishnamacharya said he had learned from a yoga teacher in Tibet. Krishnamacharya's first writings, which cited the Stitattvanidhi as a source, also featured vinyasa that Krishnamacharya said he had learned from a yoga teacher in Tibet. So the practice of the postures in India does not extend to ancient times and did not begin in India with Hinduism but with Buddhism and Buddhism was associated with the Ancient Egyptian city of Memphis where postures and spiritual magic were practiced previously.

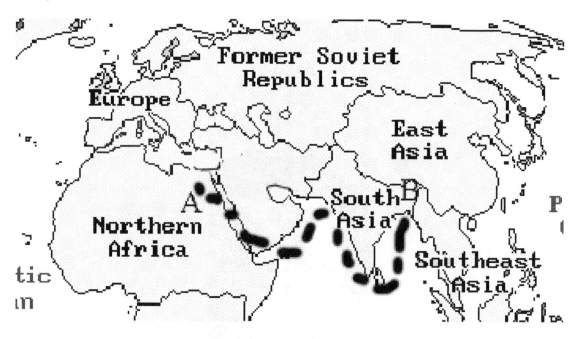

Above: (A) Egypt and (B) Tibet

Sakkara/Memphis

Above: *Djozer Pyramid Complex* with the *Step Pyramid of Imhotep* located in Sakkara, Egypt– From the Old Kingdom Period – Third Dynasty- School of Memphite Theology- based on the Divinity *Ptah.* The Tantric magical teachings and the Ancient Egyptian postures were absorbed by Tantric Buddhists and that teaching would become Hatha Yoga in Tibet and India and Kung Fu Tai Chi and Chi Kung in China.

TANTRIC BUDDHIST "MAGIC" YOGA (Tibet – India)

Buddhism Shaolin-Kung Fu Tai-Chi Chi Kung (China)

Bodhiharma

Buddhist Colony in Sakkara Egypt

The African Origins of Hatha Yoga

In ancient Kamit (Egypt) the practice of "magic", not the modern entertainment of prestidigitation for entertainment, but the discipline of spiritual practice to transform the personality from lower consciousness to higher, was legendary. Buddhism originally did not have a Tantric tradition but in the early part of the first millennium B.C.E. it developed one. That period was after the direct contact with the teachings of Ancient Egypt.

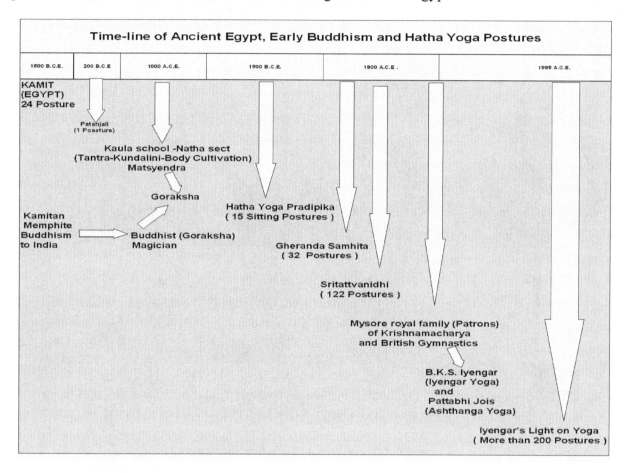

This timeline indicates the early process of evolution of Hatha Yoga in India. Hatha Yoga is said to have been originated from the Buddhist Tantric practitioners. The discipline of spiritual postures was already practiced, along with, spiritual magic, in Ancient Egypt when the Buddhist practitioners arrived in Egypt. It shows the dates in which the practice of spiritual postures was enjoined in Africa and Asia. The earliest recorded evidence for the practice of specific movements that lead to spiritual enlightenment occurs in Ancient Egypt (Kamit) c. 10,000 B.C.E. The earliest recorded practice in India of the yoga postures is c. 1,000 A.C.E.

The following list summarizes the dates in which the practice of spiritual postures was enjoined in Africa and Asia. The earliest recorded evidence for the practice of specific movements that lead to spiritual enlightenment occurs in Ancient Egypt (Kamit) c. 10,000 B.C.E. The earliest recorded practice in India of the yoga postures is c. 1,000 A.C.E.

Timeline Summary (1800 B.C.E.-1000 A.C.E.)

1,800 B.C.E. Ancient Egypt – Discipline of Sema Paut-Egyptian Yoga Postures, Arat Shetaut Neter (Goddess Mysteries), Arat Sekhem (Serpent Power), Hekau ("Magic)
Already ancient.

550 B.C.E. Cambyses invades Egypt – Buddhism, Jainism, Pythagoreaninsm, Zoroastrianism,

44

Confucianism, Taoism - BORN

261 B.C.E. Buddhist associations with Ancient Egypt – colony in Memphis.

100 A.C.E. -Tantrism – Emerges as a Distinct culture of Spirituality in Hinduism, Buddhism and Jainism Emphasizing Shaktism (Goddess female energy and Goddess as female aspect of the Absolute), Occultism, Magic, Kundalini

c. 460-490 A.C.E. Shakta and Tantra Spirituality -Writings elaborating on Tantric spirituality and mysticism of the Chakras

1000 A.C.E. -Goraksha – Develops Hatha Yoga to "Force" the movement of Kundalini (serpent Power) # of Postures?

1995 A.C.E. Iyengar developed more than 200 postures.

Hatha Yoga in the West

Many people do not know that when the practice of Hatha Yoga was adopted by yogis (one who studies the yoga disciplines) in India in the first millennium A.C.E., it was repudiated by the established practitioners of Yoga, so Indian Yoga did not originally incorporate Hatha Yoga. When it was opened up to the general community and ceased to be a practice of secluded yogis and was later brought to the west at the turn of the 20th century much later, it was not quickly adopted. However, in the latter part of the 20th century, due to the ardent promotion by a few Indian masters, it gained wide notoriety. However, for the most part only the physical benefits have been adopted and acknowledged while the mystical teachings within the discipline have not been embraced generally. Beyond the misinformed and the dogmatic followers of orthodox religion, who repudiate yoga as an occult, evil practice, one comment by a famous personality in late 20th century western culture typifies the feeling of the vast majority of those who are involved in yoga for the physical "benefits" other than "spiritual" aspects of yoga:

"I don't want it to change my life, just my butt."

-famous actress, Julia Roberts **(United States-2000 A.C.E.)****

Most practice of yoga in the western countries, especially in the United States of America, is relegated to workouts for physical benefit. This may be because people are too caught up in their daily lives, or because they feel that the true spiritual aspects of yoga would conflict with their faith-based religions. The following passages demonstrate how some Christians view yoga in the West.[32]

Some Christians have changed the practice of yoga to accommodate their own approach to spirituality and out of concern for associating with spiritual practices of other non-Christian religions.[33]/[34]/[35]

Some Christians oppose major components of yoga outright. According to Donal O'Mathuna, Ph.D., and Walt Larimore, M.D., in their book *Alternative Medicine*, they claim: "Yoga is an alternative therapy that is difficult to wholeheartedly accept or reject. As a set of physical and breathing exercises, it can improve general well-being. As a deeply religious practice with the goal of union with the divine, it is antithetical to biblical Christianity."[36]

45

Very often practitioners are arranged in large groups in cramped quarters where they are led through particular series of postures. Some forms of western yoga even use heated rooms to promote weight loss or heightened life force, etc., practices not done in India. Many times, yoga sessions have been reduced to social events where people try to impress each other or meet others in hopes of starting a romantic association. Instances have been reported where yoga instructors and students retire to a separate room in order to have sex, while other students are left to continue practicing postures without the instructor. Often women may be seen at such sessions wearing spandex or some tight fitting outfits that some more traditional practitioners have objected to. Yet, we may recall that in the Ancient Egyptian practice it was common for females and males to go about topless, not having the western conditioning of lust, shame or embarrassment regarding the physical body. However, the ancient culture is not to be confuced with the modern invention in western culture of "Naked Yoga" or Yoga practice without clothes. In modern times, due to that conditioning, along with modern stresses, general practice has necessitated forms of clothing that would incite lower desires.

Above: A Modern day Hatha Yoga Class in the West

Nevertheless, there are many in the West who have sought to discover the more spiritual or religious aspects of Indian Yoga.

Above: Hatha Yoga teacher at Hindu temple practicing yoga posture.

In recent years practitioners of Yoga became concerned about the Western predilection for copyrighting and appropriating yoga postures and claiming them for their own systems of practice. The term Yoga Piracy began to be used and moves in Inida began for the purpose of countering the piracy.

> **Yoga piracy** is the <u>appropriation</u> of postures and techniques that are found in ancient and traditional yoga treatises belonging to Hinduism and India. India yogis have been concerned by such people as fitness instructors in the West who claim <u>patents</u> and <u>copyrights</u> on asanas (yoga poses), pranayama techniques and sequences, and ayurvedic medicine. Typically, western practitioners and teachers have taken over the <u>traditional knowledge</u>, although the case of <u>Bikram Yoga</u> is also relevant.
>
> The Government of India has initiated the documentation of 1,500 yoga asana or postures - from Patanjali (ancient Hindu texts) to the present times - and is storing them in a Digital Traditional Knowledge Library to be made available to <u>patent offices</u> globally. One-third of the estimated 30 million database pages have already been compiled under the <u>Commerce Ministry</u>. Fifteen of the most prominent yoga schools in India are involved including the <u>Iyengar Institute</u> and <u>Kaivalyadham</u>, run by Nitin Unkule.
>
> While knowledge about <u>yoga</u> has been in <u>public domain</u> in India in various vernacular languages, the same was not available to patent examiners abroad, which is why outsiders have been granted patents on something that has been around in India for thousands of years.
>
> <u>New Delhi</u>'s action assumes significance as there is huge money involved in yoga, which according to some estimates, is a $3 <u>billion</u> industry in the US alone.[37]

Still, it must be understood that many people who are leading a worldly life are first introduced to yoga through the discipline of the postures in ordinary sessions dedicated to promoting physical health and later turn towards the spiritual aspects. However, there is much concern among advanced practitioners of Yoga in India and elsewhere, that Western culture has appropriated yoga and converted it to something other than yoga as it has been known for thousands of years. Instead of having Geb or Parvati as the role models, such prominent (worldly) personalities as actors and entertainers Julia Roberts, Madonna, Woody Haroldson and others have become the "ideal." So now, the same materialistic pursuits (physical health, beauty, sex-appeal, excitement, etc.), which are the hallmarks of western culture, have been projected on yoga by westerners who have appointed themselves as the purveyors of yoga to the masses. Many also distribute a myriad of products which are not necessary or desirable for the practice of yoga postures such as spandex, props, lotions, bikini yoga, etc., and conduct not spiritual yoga retreats but yoga vacations, yoga parties and the like. Yoga originated as a non-secular spiritual discipline for transcending the world and has now been converted by many into a means to enjoy the worldly pleasures more intensely. This deviation from spiritual discipline to an instrument for enhancing worldly pleasure-seeking is perhaps most prominently visible in the discipline of Tantra Yoga. Using sexual symbolism to drive home a mystical teaching, Tantra Yoga has less to do with physical sexual intercourse between human beings than intercourse of the soul with the Divine. Yet, many so called practitioners of Tantra Yoga in the west tirelessly promote the idea that it is a form of "Sex-Yoga" designed to attain spiritual enlightenment and the heights of worldly pleasure at the same time. There are many misconceptions about the history and teaching of yoga and this is perhaps one of the most blatant. The hedonistic* path of life, which typifies western culture, has been shown to be ultimately a dead end street leading to frustration and regret in later life. Yet people follow blindly the inane statements of ignorant religious leaders, entertainers, politicians, marketers and advertisers, which lead to spiritual and worldly bankruptcy.

Many practitioners of the Hatha Yoga postures do not realize that the postures were not designed just to promote physical health. Actually, like the Kemetic system, the Hindu Yoga posture system is also designed to relate a human being to the gods and goddesses and the cosmic forces, which are symbolized by the use of animal names and visualizations using natural objects. This is accomplished by the practice of the movements, study of the mythology and philosophy behind them and meditative absorption with the principles and energies that they represent. The promotion of health is only a means to an end, a byproduct of the practice, and not an end in itself. The ultimate goal of yoga is to awaken the spiritual consciousness. Any other use of yoga is a misuse or at least a limited use. In these respects the movement systems of Kemet from Ancient Egypt, Yoga from India, and Kung Fu of China, are unique when compared to other forms of exercise, movement systems. Western forms of exercise are designed to cultivate the external muscles and physical energy while the Eastern and African disciplines are designed to develop and cultivate the internal life force, which transcends physicality and the world itself.

It should be remembered that the true purpose of the yoga postures is supposed to be to enhance the capacity of the practitioner to engage in the disciplines of yogic philosophy and meditation so as to attain "Enlightenment." Physical health is only a temporary development that may be experienced as long as the body lasts, until death; so that should be thought of as a side benefit and not as a goal.

"Enlightenment means attaining that sublime and highest goal of life which is complete Self-knowledge, to experience the state of conscious awareness of oneness with the Divine and all Creation which transcends individuality born of ego consciousness...like the river uniting with the ocean, discovering the greater essential nature of Self... that state which bestows abiding blessedness, peace, bliss, contentment, fulfillment, freedom from all limitation and supreme empowerment."

NOTES:

Yoga Journal, {The New Yoga} January/February 2000

Hatha-Yoga-Pradipika, _The Shambhala Encyclopedia of Yoga_ by Georg Feuerstein, Ph. D.

The Shambhala Encyclopedia of Yoga by Georg Feuerstein, Ph. D.

The Shambhala Encyclopedia of Yoga by Georg Feuerstein, Ph. D.

Yoga Journal, {The New Yoga} January/February 2000

COMPARISON OF SOME OF THE YOGIC POSTURES
IN ANCIENT EGYPT AND INDIA

Kemetic (Egyptian) Cobra

Indian Full Cobra

Kemetic Wheel

Indian Wheel

Kemetic Spinal Twist

Indian Spinal Twist

Kemetic Lotus

Indian Lotus

Table on next page: A Timeline of the Discipline of Physical Postures in Ancient Egypt and India

20th Century A.C.E.

1. Ananda Yoga (Swami Kriyananda)
2. Anusara Yoga (John Friend)
3. Ashtanga Yoga (K. Pattabhi)
4. Ashtanga Yoga (Pattabhi Jois)
5. Bikram Yoga (Bikram Choudhury)
6. Integral Yoga (Swami Satchidananda b.
7. Iyengar Yoga (B.K.S. Iyengar)
8. Kripalu Yoga (Amrit Desai)
9. Kundalini Yoga (Yogi Bhajan)
10. Sivananda Yoga (Swami Vishnu-devananda)
11. Svaroopa Yoga (Rama Berch)

Women first admitted to Hatha Yoga practice

1893 A.C.E.	World Parliament of Religions – Vedanta Introduced to the West
1750 A.C.E.	Shiva Samhita – Hatha Yoga text – melds Vedanta with Hatha
1539 A.C.E	Birth of Sikhism
1350 A.C.E.	Hatha Yoga Pradipika text - India
1000 A.C.E.	Goraksha – Siddha Yogis First Indian Hatha Yoga Practice
600 A.C.E.	Birth of Islam
Year 0	Birth of Jesus – Christianity
300 B.C.E.	Arat, Geb, Nut Egyptian Yoga Postures – Late Period
1,680 B.C.E.	Geb, Nut, Ra, Asar, Aset, Sobek Egyptian Yoga Postures – New Kingdom
2,000 B.C.E.	Indus Valley – Kundalini – Serpent Power-Lotus Pose
3,600 B.C.E.	Nefertem Egyptian Yoga Posture – Old-Middle Kingdom Period
10,000 B.C.E.	Serpent Power-Horemakhet Egyptian Yoga Posture – Ancient Egyptian

Pre Common Era
(B.C.E.)
Developments in Physical Yoga Disciplines

Year 0	**Birth of Jesus – Christianity**
300 B.C.E.	**Arat, Geb, Nut Egyptian Yoga Postures – Late Period**
1,680 B.C.E.	**Geb, Nut, Ra, Asar, Aset, Sobek Egyptian Yoga Postures – New Kingdom**
2,000 B.C.E.	**Indus Valley – Kundalini – Serpent Power-Lotus Pose**
3,600 B.C.E.	**Nefertem Egyptian Yoga Posture – Old-Middle Kingdom Period**
10,000 B.C.E.	**Serpent Power-Horemakhet Egyptian Yoga Posture – Ancient Egyptian**

Post Common Era
(A.C.E.) Developments in Physical Yoga Disciplines

20th Century A.C.E.

1. **Ananda Yoga** (Swami Kriyananda)
2. **Anusara Yoga** (John Friend)
3. **Ashtanga Yoga** (K. Pattabhi)
4. **Ashtanga Yoga** (Pattabhi Jois)
5. **Bikram Yoga** (Bikram Choudhury)
6. **Integral Yoga** (Swami Satchidananda b.
7. **Iyengar Yoga** (B.K.S. Iyengar)
8. **Kripalu Yoga** (Amrit Desai)
9. **Kundalini Yoga** (Yogi Bhajan)
10. **Sivananda Yoga** (Swami Vishnu-devananda)
11. **Svaroopa Yoga** (Rama Berch)

Women first admitted to Hatha Yoga practice

> Virtually all modern systems of Hatha Yoga in India were invented within the last 100 years. Women were only admitted to the practice recently also.

1893 A.C.E.	**World Parliament of Religions – Vedanta Introduced to the West**
1750 A.C.E.	**Shiva Samhita – Hatha Yoga text –melds Vedanta with Hatha**
1539 A.C.E.	**Birth of Sikhism**
1350 A.C.E.	**Hatha Yoga Pradipika text -India**
1000 A.C.E.	**Goraksha – Siddha Yogis First Indian Hatha Yoga Practice**
600 A.C.E.	**Birth of Islam**
Year 0	**Birth of Jesus – Christianity**

Important events:

Goraksha - 1000 ACE – First "Human" (Indian) Teacher of Hatha Yoga

200 BCE – 500ACE Patanjali Yoga Sutras
        Asana = seated pose only (for meditation)

Detailed History of the Discipline of Physical Postures in Ancient Egypt and India from Ancient to Modern times

Smai Tawi Tjef Neteru Yoga Practice in Ancient Egypt	Hatha Yoga Practice in Ancient India and the dates when introduced
1. Horemacket (Sphinx 10,000 B.C.E.) 2. 18th Dynasty Papyri 1580 B.C.E. 3. Tomb of Hatshepsut 1580 B.C.E. 4. Temple and Tomb of Seti I (reigned 1306-1290) 5. Tomb of Queen Nefertari (reigned 1,279-1,212 BC), 6. Temple of Heru (800-300 B.C.E.), 7. Temple of Aset (800-300 B.C.E.) 8. Temple of Hetheru (400-300 B.C.E.) 9. Independent Mystery traditions (3rd century to 20th century. 10. Tjef Neteru Sema Paut (Movement of the Gods and Goddesses) 20th century *Women practiced the postures since the most ancient times.	1. **Sage Goraksha** 10th century A.C.E. (First Introduced) 2. ***Hatha-Yoga-Pradipika ("Light on the Forceful Yoga).*** It was authored by Svatmarama Yogin in mid. 14th century C.E. 3. **Shiva Samhita** – Hatha Yoga text –melds Vedanta with Hatha 1750 A.C.E. 4. Women first admitted to Hatha Yoga practice (Late 19th century 5. <u>**Modern Practices in India and the West**</u> 6. **Ananda Yoga** (Swami Kriyananda) 20th Century 7. **Anusara Yoga** (John Friend) 20th Century 8. **Ashtanga Yoga** (Pattabhi Jois) 20th Century 9. **Bikram Yoga** (Bikram Choudhury) 20th Century 10. **Integral Yoga** (Swami Satchidananda) 20th Century 11. **Iyengar Yoga** (B.K.S. Iyengar) 20th Century 12. **Kripalu Yoga** (Amrit Desai) 20th Century 13. **Kundalini Yoga** (Yogi Bhajan) 20th Century 14. **Sivananda Yoga** (Swami Vishnu-devananda) 20th Century 15. **Svaroopa Yoga** (Rama Berch) 20th Century 16. **TriYoga,** (Kali Ray) 20th Century 17. **Viniyoga** (T.K.V. Desikachar) 20th Century

Some important developments and limitations in Indian Hatha Yoga history:

1600 ACE Gheranda Samhita, another such manual, lists only 32. Conspicuously missing are the standing poses-Triangle, Warrior, etc.-and Sun Salutations that form the backbone of most contemporary systems.

1300 ACE Hatha Yoga Pradipika- the ultimate classical hatha yoga manual-lists only 15 asanas (most of them variations of the crosslegged sitting position), for which it gives very sketchy instructions.

1000 ACE – Goraksha - First "Human" (non mythic Indian) Teacher of Hatha Yoga

Thus it is evident that the practice of the Yoga postures in Egypt began over 2500 years before the practice commenced in India. It is also likely that the Indians were introduced to the system when they connected with the Ancient Egyptians during the period of the reign of the Indian Sage King Ashoka. (See the book *African Origins of Civilization, Religion and Yoga Spirituality* by Muata Ashby.)

It has been suggested that the practice of the Hatha Yoga in India began with the use of the Lotus, which may be traced to the Indus Valley culture. Also, the use of the term "Asana" or posture, by the Indian Sage Patanjali, who wrote the classical yoga treatise "Yoga Sutras" which are also known as "Ashtanga Yoga" or eight legged path or steps of yoga. The use of the lotus pose in the Indus Valley culture seems only to relate to the iconography of meditation. This is also true for the Yoga Sutras. Patanjali refers to asana as a means to practice effective meditation and not as a concerted system and series of postures for promoting health and the development of the inner Life Force. Thus, Hatha Yoga as we know it today began at the end of the first millennium of our era and not in the time before the Common Era (B.C.E.). So Ancient Egypt appears to be the source for the discipline of postures. These were practiced by the priests and priestesses in order to promote physical health but more so to promote a meditative state of mind that would allow them to come closer to the cosmic forces represented by the divinities in the iconography of the postures, thereby allowing them to discover their own divine essence and ultimately the source of all the cosmic forces, the Supreme Self.

The Ancient Egyptian Temple, the Serpent Power and the Lotus Posture

T he term "Hatha Yoga" means Forceful Yoga". Specifically, it means yoga, that is, the movement of union of the lower self with the higher, that is artificially enhanced through certain postures. What most practitioners do not realize is that what is supposed to be getting forced is the Life Force energy of the body, known as "Kundalini" in India and "Sekhem" in Ancient Egyptian practice. The practice of cultivation and raising of the life force was ancient in Egypt by the time that the term "yoga" was used in India to signify the movement towards enlightenment through union of the lower and higher self. The practice in Ancient Egypt was so much a part of the teaching of Ancient Egyptian "Sema" (Yoga) that it was embedded in the architecture of the temples themselves.

In India, the serpent power teachings began to be recoded in the Shakta and Tantra Spirituality - Writings elaborating on Tantric spirituality and mysticism of the Chakras. In Ancient Egypt the teaching of the Serpent Power was in existence at the time of the creation of the Great Sphinx (10,000 B.C.E.)

The Serpent Power Philosophy and Iconography in Ancient Egypt and India

History of the Serpent Power in Ancient Egypt

The Serpent Power teaching, known as Kundalini Yoga in India, was understood and practiced in Ancient Egypt. It is the teaching related to understanding the psychology of the human soul and personality as it relates to spiritual evolution. It is tied to the science of the Psycho-spiritual energy centers and the three main conduits of the Life Force energy, known as Sekhem in Ancient Egypt.[38]

Below left: Frontal Close Up View of the Great Sphinx. Below right: Cobra of the Great Sphinx now in the British Museum

The origins of the Serpent Power teaching in Ancient Egypt go back to the inception of Ancient Egyptian civilization. This is proven by the fact that the oldest Ancient Egyptian monument bears the emblem of the Serpent Power tradition. The Ancient Egyptian Great Sphinx once had a massive head of a cobra perched on its forehead. It is now in the British Museum. However, we know that the positioning of the serpent symbol relates to the Serpent Power teaching because a scripture describing the Serpent Power movement and how it leads a human being to spiritual evolution was discovered among various papyri related to the rituals of the Kamitan Temple. (translation by Muata Ashby)

ORIGINAL SERPENT POWER TEXT TRANSLATION

Wadjit comes to you in the form of the Serpent Goddess to anoint you on your head.

She is the mistress of fire.

She is also the double goddess Wadjit and Nekhebit.

They rise up to your head through the left side and through the right side also and shine there on the top of your head.

Not with words (in silence, stillness) they rise to the top of your head encompassing all time, as they do for their father Ra.

They speak to you from within and illumine those becoming venerable Blessed Spirits.

It is they who give souls perfection, as they work their way, up to the brow, to their dwelling place on the brow, which is their throne.

They firmly establish themselves on your brow as they do on Ra's brow.

Not leaving, taking away the enlightenment, they stay there for you forever.

The Pharaonic headdress tradition visible in Ancient Egyptian culture from the headdress of the Sphinx in the Pre-Dynastic era to the early Christian era establishes a Serpent Power tradition and the tradition of the Pharaonic system of government in Egypt of at least 10,400 years.

Below: a diagram of the Temple of Amun-Ra at Karnak, Egypt, showing the Pylons (A), the Court (B), the Hypostyle Hall (C), the Chapel of Amun (Holy of Holies - D), the Chapel of Mut (E), the Chapel of Chons (F).

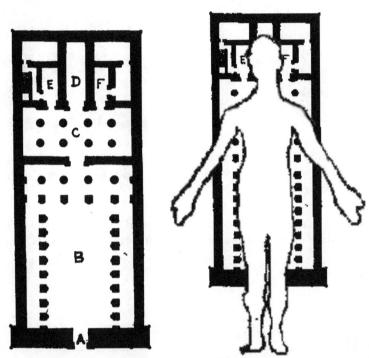

The typical Ancient Egyptian Temple incorporated the Serpent Power mysticism within its architecture. The Temple sections relate to the parts of the human anatomy as follows, and the serpentine movement is a precursor for the Hermetic Caduceus (Late Period Kamitan Philosophy).

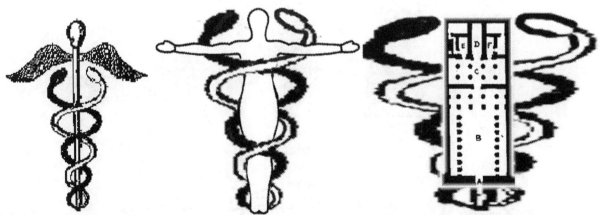

Just as it is described in the Ancient Egyptian Serpent Power scripture, the two serpents meet each other at the area of the Temple which correlates to the head of the individual human being. These sections of the Temple are known as the "great house" (left side) and the "house of fire" (right side).

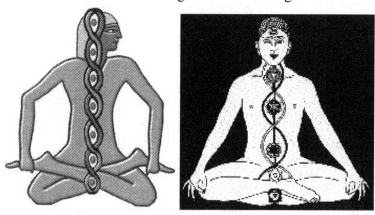

Above left: Ancient Egyptian artistic representation of the yogi seated in the lotus posture displaying the three main channels of the *Arat Shekhem* (Serpent Power) and the *Sefech Ba Ra* (7 Life Force energy centers) 5th dynasty (4th millennium B.C.E.)

Above right: Indian artistic representation of the yogi seated in the lotus posture displaying the three main channels of the Kundalini Shakti (Serpent Power) and the 7 Chakras (Life Force energy centers) 19th century A.C.E.

Table 1: The Life Force:

Ancient Egypt	India	China
Sekhem	Prana (Kundalini)	Chi

The energy centers (chakras) wherein the Life Force energy is transformed from subtle to gross energy for use by the body are seven in number and are depicted as follows.

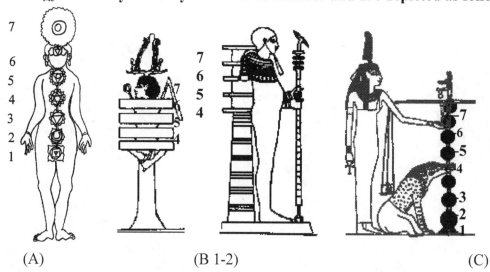

(A) (B 1-2) (C)

Figure 1: Left (A), the East Indian rendition of the Life Force energy centers (chakras) in the subtle spine of the individual.

Figure 2: Center (B 1-2), Ptah-Asar-Ancient Egyptian rendition of the Life Force energy centers in the subtle spine of the individual. The god Asar displays the four upper centers as centers of higher consciousness.

Figure 3: The figure at right (C) shows the scale of Maat displaying the seven spheres or energy centers called the *"seven souls of Ra"* and *"the seven arms of the balance (Maat)."*

Figure (C), above, includes the Ammit demon, (composite beast combining one third hippopotamus, one third lion and one third crocodile), symbolic devourer of unrighteous souls, biting between the 3rd & 4th sphere (energy center-chakra). This means that those who have not attained a consciousness level higher than the 3rd center will continue to suffer and reincarnate. The spheres represent levels of spiritual consciousness from the most ignorant (1) to the most enlightened (7). The lower three spheres are related to worldly consciousness and the upper four are related to spiritual consciousness and enlightenment, therefore, the lower must be sublimated into the higher levels. This is the project of spiritual evolution. Those who have attained higher (3rd through the 7th) will move on and attain enlightenment. This Kamitan system of energy spheres and the Caduceus with its central shaft symbolizing the subtle spine, and the two intertwining serpents, symbolizing the dual energies into which the central shaft differentiates, concurs in every detail with the later developments in East Indian Mysticism encompassed by the discipline known as Kundalini Yoga with its system of Chakras and the three main energy channels, Sushumna (central) and Ida and Pingala (intertwining conduits).

Above-An East Indian depiction of the Chakras with the Sushumna (central) and Ida and Pingala (intertwining conduits).

Above- Two Center images- left - the Hermetic[39] Caduceus with the central Shaft (Asar), and the intertwining serpents (Uadjit and Nekhebit, also known as Aset and Nebethet); right-Ancient caduceus motif: Asar with the serpent goddesses.

Above- Far Right- The Kamitan Energy Consciousness Centers (depicted as Spheres-Chakras or serpentine chains)

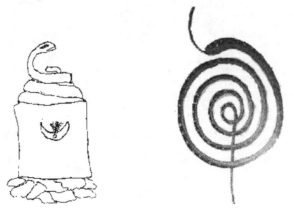

Above left: the Arat Serpent of Ancient Egyptian mysticism (Basket of Isis) showing the classic 3 ½ turns of the Serpent Power. Above right: the Kundalini Serpent of Indian mysticism showing the classic 3 ½ turns of the Serpent Power.

: Below -Stele of *Paneb*. Dyn. 19. From Dier el-Medina (Waset Egypt) He worships the serpent goddess *Mertseger* (She who loves silence) in order to propitiate her favor in the development of Transcendental awareness.[40]

Below –An Indian yoga practitioner touches his body in the areas corresponding to the Chakras in order to focus the mantras (words of power) and develop the Kundalini (Serpent Power) while worshipping the Kundalini Serpent. From Rajasthan, 1858, gauche on paper.[41]

Note: With reference to the following three pictures, review the earlier section titled "The Early Practice of Yoga in India and the Connection to Ancient Egypt."

Below- Deity with worshipers and Serpents Indus Valley, Ancient India. Recognized as possibly the oldest known depiction of Yoga in India, this image incorporates the philosophy later known as Kundalini Yoga.

Below: The Serpent goddesses Aset (Isis) and Nebethet (Nephthys) worship Asar (Osiris), Ancient Egypt, Africa. The Hawk above symbolizes raising consciousness. The two goddesses represent the Serpent Power in Kamitan mysticism from the earliest period of Ancient Egyptian history.

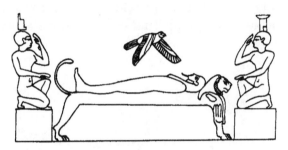

Below- The Serpent goddesses Aset (Isis) and Nebethet (Nephthys) depicted as the dual serpents with are in reality manifestations of the one singular essence.

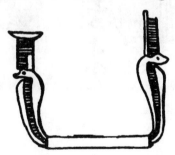

Below- Left-The Ancient Egyptian Papyrus Greenfield (British Museum) displaying the rings signifying the serpentine path of the Life Force, and the levels of spiritual consciousness (the Chakras or Psycho-spiritual consciousness centers).

Below: Papyrus Qenna (Leyden Museum), displaying the spheres signifying the serpentine path of the Life Force from the Spirit above to the heart below, and the levels of spiritual consciousness (the Chakras or Psycho-spiritual consciousness centers).

The Physical Yoga Postures Part 2

Contrary to popular knowledge, that the use of physical Yoga postures dates back to ancient times in India, the practice of the discipline that was later known, up to the present, as "Hatha Yoga" in India only began in India at around the year 1000 A.C.E. and not in pre-Christian (Comma Era) times as is commonly supposed. At that time it was associated with Tantric Buddhism. Often times the mention of the word "asana" in the Patanjali Yoga Sutras" (200 B.C.E.) is thought to represent an early practice of Hatha Yoga. However, when the statements by Patanjali are examined closely, it is clear that the meaning relates to a sitting posture for meditation and not the elaborate system of a sequence of postures designed to cultivate physical health and harmonization of the Ha (solar) and Tha (lunar) energies of the physical and astral bodies of a person.

Further, notice that the popular practices of Hatha Yoga which have come to the West are all 20th century developments. They are outgrowths of the original Hatha Yoga concept but are modern interpretations or fabrication, exemplifying elaborate and in many ways intricate concepts and practices which were not enjoined by sage Goraksha. The emphasis on the physical postures as either a discipline for physical health in a limited sense or as a self-contained end of Yoga at the exclusion of the other disciplines (meditation, study of the wisdom teachings, right action, and devotional worship) has prompted many Indian masters to complain about the disregard for the true meaning of Yoga and the true purpose of the exercise postures. As with so many other disciplines, Western society has taken cultural disciplines and traditions but ascribing new meanings and transforming these disciplines and traditions into something other than what they originally were. The practice of the Indian Hatha Yoga postures has been adopted by many in the western countries but the adjunct practice of meditation and the philosophy of the postures has been left aside in great measure. The postures are mostly used as a means to promote physical health as opposed to their original intent of promoting positive spiritual evolution. The following article illustrates this point. (text emphasis by Ashby)

TAKE A SEAT by Alan Reder

If your not meditating, are you really doing Yoga?

– Yoga Journal Feb. 2001

THE SUCCESS OF YOGA in the West may have come at a heavy price. Many teachers worry that something special has been lost in Yoga American style, and that something is meditation. Meditation, not postures, is the heart of Yoga, they point out. In Patanjali's India, Yoga and meditation were nearly synonymous, yet meditation plays only a minor role in many American Yoga courses. In others, it is not taught at all.

Some Yoga students regard meditation as boring cultural baggage and appreciate learning postures without it. But what if your experience with Yoga has inspired you to go deeper, into Yogic spirituality? If your Yoga teacher doesn't offer meditation guidance, how should you begin? Since Yoga comes from India, should your meditation technique be Hindu or Buddhist? Is Zen Buddhist okay? Does the inner peace you already feel in Yoga class count?

Records of <u>meditation as a discipline for lay people, as opposed to priests,</u> first show up about 500 B.C. in both India and China.

Contrary to what many Yoga students believe, his (Patanjali) text said little about Hatha Yoga postures, which weren't a widespread practice at the time.

> From Raja Yoga Sutras – Translated by Swami Jyotirmayananda:
>
> Samadhi Pad Sutra 46: *seated pose for meditation*
> Samadhi Pad Sutra 48-49: *perfecting the seated pose for*

The important question arises, is Yoga *(Exercise)* in the West really being practiced correctly? In fact, can it even be said that yoga is being practiced in the west? The following excerpts from an article that appeared in the magazine Yoga Journal, explores this problem.

"The New Yoga, America is Reinventing the Practice...But it is still Yoga?"
"New Light on Yoga" – Yoga Journal – July/Aug 1999

"Dr. Jayadeva Yogendra...his father, at the turn of the twentieth century, was one of the first yogic crusaders to bring hatha yoga to practices ....and begin teaching them to a lay audience. 'When I see what yoga has become I the west,'..... **'I wish my father had left it with the hermits in the caves'."**

The degradation of the practice of Yoga was typified by the comment of a well-known Hollywood Actress when she said:

I don't want Yoga to change my life, just my butt! USA – 2000 ACE
-well known Hollywood Actress- Julia Roberts

Many teachers of the Indian Yoga postures in the western countries take pride in learning the jargon of Sanskrit words and wowing their students with difficult contortions but not including philosophy or meditation in their practice, presumably because the populations of the west are hostile to forms of spirituality other than the western religions (Christianity, Islam, and Judaism). In the current climate (late 20th century-early 21st) where the social climate is increasingly religiously intolerant, the prospects of Yoga and other mystical traditions in the west will be problematical. The following guidelines should be followed if the true Indian and Ancient Egyptian tradition of the postures is to be upheld.

Integral Practice of the Yoga postures includes physical regimen, diet, philosophy, meditation, devotional practice and virtuous living.

- **Integral Practice is not just the Postures, not just meditation, not just cultivation of the vital body, not just wisdom**
- **It must include mystical philosophy, leading to entry into higher planes of existence.**
- **It is those experiences that informs all yogic movements in all religions of history.**
- **Names, jargons, clothing, memorized texts, etc. are foundations, not attainments.**

Hatha Yoga, Buddhism and Ancient Egypt

"In Zen Buddhism, for example, students can chant a lineage of teachers stretching back for centuries, with each Zen master certified by the one preceding. No such unbroken chain of transmission exists in hatha yoga. For generations, hatha yoga was a rather obscure and occult corner of the yoga realm, viewed with disdain by mainstream practitioners, kept alive by a smattering of isolated ascetics in caves and Hindu *maths* (monasteries). It appears to have existed for centuries in seed form, lying dormant and surfacing again and again. In the twentieth century, it had almost died out in India. According to his biography, Krishnamacharya had to go all the way to Tibet to find a living master…Given this lack of a clear historical lineage, how do we know what is "traditional" in hatha yoga? Where did our modern proliferation of poses and practices come from? Are they a twentieth century invention?"

-July/August 1999 By Anne Cushman (Yoga Journal)

The statements by Ms. Cushman are startling in view of the well known reputation of Yoga as a tradition of several thousands of years with a lineage going back to ancient times. It turns out that that lineage, if it can be traced anywhere in ancient times would be traced to Ancient Egypt and nowhere else. As far as its development up to the precent, Hatha Yoga **had almost died out in India until it was revived in the early twentieth century.**

From loincloths to leotards,
Yoga has come a long way in
5000 years. But is yoga as we know it
Really that old?

By Anne Cushman [Yoga Journal Magazine July/August 1999]

In a Yoga journal article, Anne Cushman explored the origins of Hatha Yoga, which is widely touted as thousands of years old. Yet upon closer investigation, Hatha Yoga [Yoga postures as developed in India] is found to be no older than 1, 006 years old [as of the year 2006] beginning with the work of Goraksha, who is widely celebrated as its inventor. It is important to note that Goraksha was a **Buddhist magician** and part of an earlier tradition of Tantric Buddhism that stretched back to the early part of the 1st milleniun A.C.E. and contact with Ancient Egypt.

Do-It-Yourself Yoga

Having articulated an Anusara philosophy with Brooks, Friend set about laying its foundation. Since Americans respond enthusiastically to easily definable categories, quick solutions, catchphrases, and simplicity, Friend boiled his system down to what he calls the "three A's": attitude, alignment, and action.

-Yoga Journal 8-20004

Is this Research Debunking Hatha Yoga?

The presentation of these articles and evidences from sources like Yoga Journal are not meant to debunk yoga itself. They are included here to debunk the erroneous notions about the origins of yoga and the misconceptions that lead to the misuse or misunderstanding about the true purpose of yoga. They are also revealing of the fact that the main purveyors in the West are aware of the short and limited history of Hatha Yoga in India and that the practice has developed away from its original practice even from the Indian perspective, let alone the Ancient Egyptian. Nevertheless, the practice of the physical postures of Yoga offers some immediate benefits:

- ✓ Physical fitness
- ✓ Sense of well-being
- ✓ Feeling of moving towards something greater

However, most practitioners are content with that. Are these attainments the goal of Yoga? No, the true purpose is to lead a practitioner to spiritual enlightenment. All other benefits are secondary. Yet most practitioners in the West use yoga only for the physical benefits.

The distortion of even the purpose of yoga as taught in India in the early 20th century caused some of the original practitioners who brought it to the west to regret what they had done as they saw the practice being adulterated and innovations made by Western practitioners.

Many practitioners of Indian Hatha Yoga are fond of describing their practice as "ancient" and as being comprised of an unbroken "lineage" of teachers going back "thousands of years." Upon close examination of the practice in India we find that no such unbroken chain of transmission exists in Hatha Yoga. Actually in the early twentieth century, it had almost died out in India.

> HATHA-YOGA ("forceful Yoga"), also called hatha-vidya ("science of hatha"); the type of Yoga specific to the Kanphata sect, though this designation is also applied in general to the vast body of doctrines and practices geared toward Self-realization by means of perfecting the body.

The term Hatha Yoga is defined as "forceful union," that is forcing spiritual evolution via the cultivation of the energies of the physical body. In Ancient Egypt the program of transformation through body cultivation was described in the Pert M Heru text, more commonly known as the Egyptian Book of the Dead, as well as in other texts.

The origins of Hatha Yoga were clearly in Buddhism and not in Hinduism since we find evidence of rejection of Hatha Yoga by the Hindu sages. **Hatha Yoga is clearly rejected in the Laghu -Yoga - Vasishtha (5.6.86, 92), which maintains that it merely leads to pain. <u>Some of criticisms are especially against the magical undercurrents.</u>**

> **<u>GORAKSHA or GORAKSHANATHA</u>** The most popular teacher of hathayoga, who is widely celebrated as its inventor, is Goraksha (9th or 10th cen. CE), a member of the Natha tradition, in which body cultivation played a crucial role. He is acclaimed by some as the first writer of Hindi or Punjabi prose and is credited with the authorship of numerous works, including the Goraksha-Samhit4, the Amaraugha-Prabodha, the Jnata-Amrita-Shastra, and the Siddha-

SiddhantaPaddhati. Although the Tibetan sources speak of him as a Buddhist magician, the works ascribed to him and his school have a distinct leaning toward Shaivism. [42]

The most popular teacher of hathayoga, who is widely celebrated as its inventor, is **Goraksha** (9th or 10th cen. CE), a member of the Natha tradition, in which body cultivation played a crucial role. In India it came under attack early in its development. For instance, it is clearly rejected in the Laghu -Yoga - Vasishtha (5.6.86, 92), which maintains that it merely leads to pain. The most formidable critic of hatha-yoga was Vijndna Bhikshu, a sixteenth- century savant and Yoga practitioner. Some of his criticisms, especially against the magical undercurrents present in this yogic approach, are undoubtedly justified. [43]

Tantrism and the Origins of the Physical Yoga Postures Part 1 : Introduction to Tantrism

Recognition of "Egyptian" Tantra practice by Indian practitioners.

Tantrism and Tantric Magical practice is a source discipline from which the concept of Hatha Yoga developed. In his book, Ajit Mookerjee acknowledged the existence of Tantrism in Ancient Egypt.

Tantric Philosophy:

> Tantric influence, however, is not limited to India alone, and there is evidence that the precepts of tantrism traveled to various parts of the world, especially Nepal, Tibet, China, Japan and parts of South-East Asia; its influence has also been evident in Mediterranean cultures such as those of Egypt and Crete.[44]
> -Ajit Mookerjee (Indian Scholar-Author –from the book *The Tantric Way*)

Hatha Yoga in India was started by practitioners of Tantrism, specifically, Tantric Buddhists. Tantra Yoga is purported to be the oldest system of Yoga. Tantra Yoga is a system of Yoga which seeks to promote the re-union between the individual and the Absolute Reality, through the worship of nature and ultimately the Cosmos as an expression of the Absolute. Since nature is an expression of GOD, it gives clues as to the underlying reality that sustains it and the way to achieve wisdom, i.e. transcendence of it. The most obvious and important teaching that nature holds is the idea that creation is made up of pairs of opposites: Up-down, here-there, you-me, us-them, hot-cold, male-female, Ying-Yang, etc. The interaction of these two complementary opposites we call life and movement.

Insight (wisdom) into the true nature of reality gives us a clue as to the way to realize the oneness of creation within ourselves. Tantra is a recognition of the male and female nature of Creation as a reflection of the male and female nature of the Divine which were brought together to create the universe. By re-uniting the male and female principles in our own bodies and minds, we may reach the oneness that underlies our apparent manifestation as a man or woman. Thus, the term Tantra means to create a bridge between the opposites and in so doing, the opposites dissolve, leaving unitary and transcendental consciousness. The union of the male and female principles may be effected by two individuals who worship GOD through GOD's manifestation in each other or by an individual who seeks union with GOD through uniting with his or her female or male spiritual principles, respectively, within themselves. All men and women have both female and male principles within themselves.

In the Egyptian philosophical system, all Neteru or God principles emanate from the one GOD. When these principles are created, they are depicted as having a ***male and female*** principle. All objects and life forms appear in creation as either male or female, but underlying this apparent duality, there is a unity which is rooted in the pure consciousness of oneness, the consciousness of the Transcendental Divine, which underlies and supports all things. To realize this oneness consciously deep inside is the supreme goal.

In Tantrism, sexual symbolism is used frequently because these are the most powerful images denoting the opposites of Creation and the urge to unify and become whole, for sexuality is the urge for unity and self-discovery, albeit limited to physical intercourse by most people. If this force is understood, harnessed and sublimated it will lead to unity of the highest order that is unity with the Divine Self.

Above- The Kamitan God Geb and the Kamitan Goddess Nut separate after the sexual union that gave birth to the gods and goddesses and Creation. Figure 4: Below: Three depictions of the god Asar in tantric union with Aset.

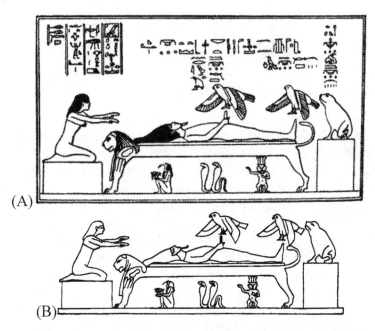

Above-(A) and (B) Reliefs from Ancient Egyptian Temples of the virgin birth of Heru (Horus) - The resurrection of Asar (Osiris) - Higher Self, Heru consciousness). Isis in the winged form hovers over the reconstructed penis of the dead Asar.

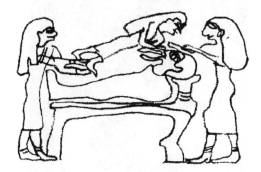

Drawing found in an Ancient Egyptian Building of The Conception of Heru[45]-*From a Stele at the British Museum 1372. 13th Dyn.*

Above: Goddess Aset (Isis), of Ancient Egypt, (representing the physical body-creation) and the dead body of Asar (representing the spirit, that essence which vivifies matter) are shown in symbolic immaculate union (compare to the "Kali Position" on the following page) begetting Heru, symbolizing to the immaculate conception which takes place at the birth of the spiritual life in every human: the birth of the soul (Ba) in a human is the birth of Horus.

Above- the god Shiva and his consort Shakti

The "Kali position" (above) features **Shiva and Shakti (Kundalini-Prakriti)** in divine union (India). As with Aset and Asar of Egypt, Shiva is the passive, male aspect who "gives" the life essence (Spirit) and creative impetus and Shakti is energy, creation, the active aspect of the Divine. Thus Creation is akin to the idea of the Divine making love with him/herself. Shiva and Shakti are the true essence of the human being, composed of spirit and matter (body). In the active aspect, the female is in the "active" position while the male is in the "passive" position. Notice in the pictures above and below that the females are in the top position and the males are on the bottom. In Kamitan philosophy, the god Geb is the earth and the goddess Nut is the sky. Just as the earth is sedentary and the sky is dynamic, so too are the divinities depicted in this way in Southern (African) and Eastern (India) iconography. Notice that the female divinities are always on the top position. This is classic in Eastern and Kamitan mysticism. It is a recognition that the spirit (male aspect) is sedentary while matter, the female aspect, is in perpetual motion, and the two complement and complete each other.

Above- Buddha and his consort. Tibetan Buddhist representation of The Dharmakaya, the cosmic father-mother, expressing the idea of the Supreme Being as a union of both male and female principals.

Tantric philosophy makes use of sexual imagery to convey the teaching of the principle of the opposites in creation as well as the principle of all encompassing divinity. Sexuality encompasses the entire creation and any symbol that denotes all-encompassing divinity is a tantric symbol. The phallic symbols as well as the winged disk and the multi-armed divinity all symbolize all-encompassing divinity.

Below left- The Triune ithyphallic form of Asar.[46]

Below right- the Trilinga (Triune ithyphallic form) of Shiva.[47]

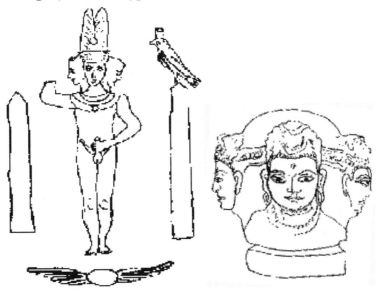

The Winged Sundisk of Heru – Kamitan.

Below - the multi-armed (all-pervasive) dancing Shiva-whose dance sustains the Creation.

Below- left Ashokan[48] pillar with lion capital-Kamitan pillar with lion capitals. Center: Ancient Egyptian pillar with lion capitals. Far right: the Ethiopian divinity Apedemak, displaying the same leonine trinity concept and the multi-armed motif.

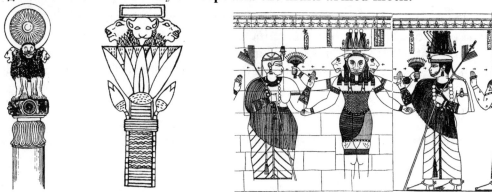

The trinity symbolically relates the nature of the Divine, who is the source and sustenance of the three worlds (physical, astral and causal), the three states of consciousness (conscious, subconscious and unconscious), the three modes of nature (dull, agitated and lucid), the three aspects of human experience (seer, seen and sight), as well as the three stages of initiation (ignorance, aspiration and enlightenment). This triad idea is common to Neterianism, and Hinduism.

The idea of the multi-armed divinity is common in Indian Iconography. However, the depiction above from Ethiopia spiritual iconography shows that it was present in Africa as well.

Tantrism and the Origins of the Physical Yoga Postures: Part 2 - Introduction to Tantrism, Magic and the Postures of Yoga

Tantric philosophy figures prominently in the origins of Indian Hatha Yoga as one of its disciplines. As was discussed earlier, Tantrism was practiced in Ancient Egypt from the earliest times. The practice of Tantrism in Ancient Egypt was akhnowledged by Ajit Mookerjee.

> Tantric influence, however, is not limited to India alone, and there is evidence that the precepts of tantrism traveled to various parts of the world, especially Nepal, Tibet, China, Japan and parts of South-East Asia; its influence has also been evident in Mediterranean cultures such as those of Egypt and Crete.
> -Ajit Mookerjee (Indian Scholar-Author –from the book *The Tantric Way*)

Specifically, Tantric Buddhism gave rise to the earliest practice of certain postures as a means to enhance spiritual evolution. Before this time, the only reference to Asana or posture was the sitting posture for meditation, mentioned in the Raja Yoga Sutras by Patanjali.

There is clear evidence of the existence of tantric thought in the Sakkara/Memphis- School of Memphite Theology- Divinity *Ptah*. There is also clear evidence of the practice of "magic" or "Hekau" and the practice of Tjef Neteru or postures of the gods and goddesses in Egypt.[49]

Below: Cultural-religious exchange between Egypt and India in the time of Emperor Ashoka in 261 B.C.E. Tracing the movement of "Egyptian Tantric Magic" from Memphis in Ancient Egypt to India.

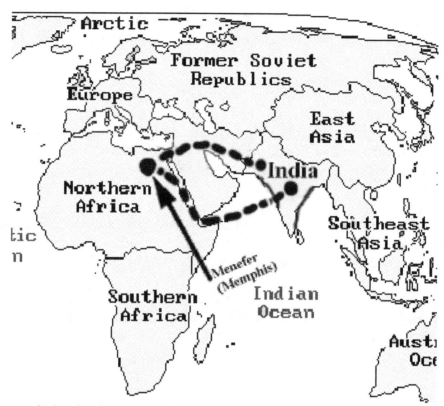

In the chapter of the book *India and Egypt: Influences and Interactions*, 1993, entitled *Transmission of Ideas and Imagery*, the scholar M. C. Joshi reports on ancient written documents attesting to the communications and cultural exchanges between Ancient Egypt and India during the time of the Indian emperor Ashoka.

In the book Search for the Buddha by Charles Allen, the author documents the Buddhist connection to Ancient Egypt as follows. The Buddhist/Indian ruler had a practice of setting up pillars with inscriptions attesting to his following the Buddhist principles and other edicts. One was discovered that unequivocally shows that ancient Egypt and India were associated.

In March 1838 a more complete and accurate impression of the Girnar rock inscription became available to James Prinsep. On 14 'March he wrote another of those letters to Alexander Cunningham that bubble over with enthusiasm and good cheer. The Girnar inscription differed from the pillar edicts in a number of passages, and in one he had found a line that linked Piyadasi/Ashoka to Egypt and the Ptolemys:

The passage in the 14th edict is much mutilated, and I long for a more correct copy. It really becomes interesting to find Egypt and Ptolemy known to Asoka! I must give you the real text:

The African Origins of Hatha Yoga

Yona raja paran cha tena chaptaro rajanan tulamayo
Greek king furthermore by whom the Gypta rajas Ptolemy
*cha antigina cha maga cha * * ***
and Antigonus and Magus and * * *
savata devanampiya dhammanusasti anubatate yata pajati
everywhere Beloved of the God's religious precept reaches
where goes.

Hurrah for inscriptions!

Here was proof of diplomatic links between Ashoka's empire and the West, in the form of Alexander the Great's successors: the Egyptian king Ptolemy was probably Ptolemy II (ruled 285-247 BCE); Antigonus was probably Antigonos Gonatos of Macedonia

TANTRIC BUDDHIST "MAGIC" YOGA begins to develop especially in Tibet – India.

In ancient Kamit there were at least 24 postures in the spiritual practice prior to the time of Patanjali. In the practice of Kamitan Tjef Neteru (Egyptian Hatha Yoga) the "magic" consists in using postures to engender certain alignments with spiritual energies and cosmic forces. This is the kind of practice repudiated by the Hindu sages and adopted by the Tantric Buddhists. Between the years 100 A.C.E. and 1000 A.C.E. the Buddhist Kaula school developed some postures. Then Goraksha developed what is regarded by present day Hatha Yoga practitioners as a practice similar to the present day. However, the number of postures only reached 15 at the time of the Hatha Yoga Pradipika scripture. The Mysore family was instrumental in the development since they were strong patrons of Hatha Yoga. Subsequent teachers developed more postures and vinyasa (which was not practiced in early Indian Hatha Yoga) up to the 20th century where there are over 200. The teacher Krishnamacharya said he had learned from a yoga teacher in Tibet. Krishnamacharya's first writings, which cited the Stitattvanidhi as a source, also featured vinyasa (sequences of poses synchronized with the breath) that Krishnamacharya said he had learned from a yoga teacher in Tibet. So the practice of the postures in India does not extend to ancient times and did not begin in India with Hinduism but with Buddhism and Buddhism was associated with the Ancient Egyptian city of Memphis where postures and spiritual magic were practiced previously.

Hatha Yoga, Vegetarianism, Asceticism and the control and Sublimation of Sexual Energy in Ancient Egypt and India

Vegetarianism and Austerity India

> **veg·e·tar·i·an·ism** *n.* The practice of subsisting on a diet composed primarily or wholly of vegetables, grains, fruits, nuts, and seeds, with or without eggs and dairy products.[50]

Vegetarianism is an integral part of Ancient Egyptian "Sema" (Yogic practices). The discipline of body cultivation requires physical purity down to the cellular level. In order for that to occur it is necessary to have a vegetarian diet. Early Indian tradition did not have a vegetarian diet component. It was not until the Jains and Buddhists developed such a teaching in association with the practice of non-violence, that Indians began to adopt vegetarian diets. Again, the Buddhists in particular, were in close association with the Ancient Egyptian priests and priestesses in Egypt. The practice of vegetarianism would have been strongly impressed on them.

The practice of vegetarianism has been noted since ancient times. The Greek historian, Herodotus, reported meeting a group of people in India who practiced vegetarianism in the 5th century B.C.E. Its purpose is to augment physical health and to promote mental clarity to engender spiritual sensitivity. However, its practice is often misunderstood and maligned, especially in Western Culture, as a boring or depressing way to live. Along with vegetarianism, the practice of fasting and prayer have also been used by religions throughout history to promote spiritual transcendence.

One of the great benefits of the introduction of Hatha Yoga into Western Culture has been to promote the discipline of vegetarianism. However, when we look at the history of Yoga and the Vedas in India we find that vegetarianism was not a Vedantic tenet. The writings of the Rig Veda show that meat eating (including beef) was common in Vedic times. It was not until the emergence of Buddhism and Jainism (6th Century B.C.E.) and their protestations related to animal sacrifices and the killing of animals for commercial purposes that Hinduism began to adopt the philosophy. Vaishnavism was among the first of the Hindu traditions to adopt vegetarianism. The practice was adopted by most but not all Hindu traditions. For example, meat eating continues in the Shaiva and Shakta traditions, some Tantric traditions and some Buddhist sects. The following exerts from the *Laws of Manu* and the *Bhagavad Gita,* the premier text on Indian Yoga philosophy, provide concise descriptions as to the nature and practice of austerity, control of the senses and sexual desires as well as the consumption of food. It is remarkably similar to the Kamitan descriptions that will follow.

Laws of Manu Chapter 2

177. Let him abstain from honey, meat, perfumes, garlands, substances (used for) flavoring (food), women, all substances turned acid, and from doing injury to living creatures.

Bhagavad Gita: Chapter 2

Samkhya Yogah--The Yoga of Knowledge

54. Arjuna said: O Krishna, what are the characteristics of the Sage who is established in Samadhi? How does he of steady wisdom sit, how does he speak, how does he walk?

55. Sri Krishna said: O Arjuna, when a man thoroughly renounces all the desires of the mind and is satisfied in the Self by the Self, he is called a man of steady wisdom.

56. He who is not agitated in the midst of sorrowful conditions and who is devoid of craving in the midst of pleasant circumstances, who is free from attachment, fear, and anger, such a Sage is called a person of steady wisdom.

57. He who is without attachment in everything and while meeting with good and evil, neither rejoices nor hates, his wisdom is established.

58. When he is able to withdraw his senses from the sense-objects, even like a tortoise that withdraws its limbs from all sides, he is then established in wisdom.

Bhagavad Gita: Chapter 4 Jnan Vibhag Yogah--The Yoga of Wisdom

20. Having renounced attachment to action and its fruits, he who is eternally contented and free from dependence, even though he may be engaged in action, does nothing at all.

21. Devoid of cravings, with the body and mind under his control, having renounced all objects of pleasure, a Yogi performs actions only to maintain the body. He does not enter into the evil of the world-process.

Bhagavad Gita: Chapter 6 Adhyadma Yogah--The Yoga of Meditation

17. If one is regulated in food and entertainment, harmonized in performing actions, and balanced in sleeping and waking, then he can perfect that Yoga which leads to the cessation of pain.

Bhagavad Gita: Chapter 17 Shraddha Traya Vibhag Yogah--the Yoga of the Division of Threefold Faith

8. The foods that promote life, mental strength, vitality, health, cheerfulness, and loving nature; which are savory, nutritious, digestible and agreeable--these are dear to the Satwicas.

9. The foods that are very bitter, sour, saltish, hot, pungent, dry (tasteless), burning; which produce pain, grief and disease are dear to the Rajasicas.[51]

The African Origins of Hatha Yoga

10. The foods that are stale, devoid of taste, foul smelling, rotten, refuse and impure are liked by those who are Tamasicas.[52]

14. Service of gods, Brahmins, Guru (spiritual preceptor) and wise men; purity, uprightness, Brahmacharya (sex-restraint), and non-violence--these are called the austerity of the body.

15. That speech which does not cause agitation in others, which is truthful, pleasant and helpful; and repeated study of scriptures--these constitute the austerity of speech.

16. Serenity of mind, gentleness, silence, control of senses, elevated feeling of the heart--these are called the austerity of the mind.

Hindu culture developed the discipline of food in the following way. Food was classified into the system of the Gunas, *Tamasik* (Dull), *Rajasik* (agitating), and *Sattwik* (balanced-harmonious-lucid). Classifications were given as to the foods which were fit for consumption by spiritual practitioners (Sattwik), and the foods which were not conducive to the development of higher consciousness (Tamasik and Rajasik). The Samkhya philosophy[53] term Sattwik relates to foods that are lucid and this of course relates to a vegetarian diet. It is derived from the term *Sattwa,* that appears in the Bhagavad Gita,[54] meaning pure, illuminating and the like.

Vegetarianism and Austerity in Ancient Egypt

The practice of vegetarianism has been associated with Hatha Yoga and yoga generally even though most Western practitioners of Yoga have ignored this part of yoga. There are several references to the practice of vegetarianism in Ancient Egypt. The cow was revered there since ancient times, well before the emergence of Hinduism as we have seen, and the general diet of the Ancient Egyptians included a mostly vegetarian diet and fasting. The dietetic concept adopted by Hippocrates, that improper foods are the cause of disease, was espoused by the Ancient Egyptians in the early Dynastic Period. The initiates were required to keep a much more restrictive dietary regimen than the general populous, which excluded not only meats, but also alcoholic beverages and carnal indulgences. These austerities constituted an advanced form of ascetic lifestyle which allowed the Ancient Egyptian initiates to pursue the paths of spiritual development, unhindered by the proclivities of the lower nature. Ancient Egyptian Temple practices led to the development of Western Monasticism in Christianity, Judaism and Islam. The following ancient texts are instructive in these disciplines.

> "The priests (of Ancient Egypt), having renounced all other occupation and human labour, devoted their whole life to contemplation and vision of things divine. By vision they achieve honour, safety and piety, by contemplation of knowledge, and through both a discipline of lifestyle which is secret and has the dignity of antiquity. Living always with divine knowledge and inspiration puts one beyond all greed, restrains the passions, and makes life alert for understanding. They practiced simplicity, restraint, self-control, perseverance and in everything justice and absence of greed.... Their walk was disciplined, and they practiced controlling their gaze, so that if they chose they did not blink. Their laughter was rare, and if did happen, did not go beyond a smile. They kept their hands always within their clothing. . . . Their lifestyle was frugal and simple. Some tasted no wine at all, others a very little: they accused it of causing damage to the nerves and a fullness in the head which impedes research, and of producing desire for sex."[55]

Plutarch outlined the teachings of the Temple of Aset (Isis-Ancient Egypt) for the proper behavior of initiates in his writings about his experiences as an initiate of (Aset) Isis. In the following excerpts Plutarch describes the purpose and procedure of the diet observed by the initiates of Aset, and the goal to be attained through the rigorous spiritual program which is in most every area equal to that which is outlined in the Bhagavad Gita, the premiere text of Indian Yoga.

> "To desire, therefore, and covet after truth, those truths more especially which concern the divine nature, is to aspire to be partakers of that nature itself (1), and to profess that all our studies and inquiries (2) are devoted to the acquisition of holiness. This occupation is surely more truly religious than any external (3) purifications or mere service of the temple can be (4). But more especially must such a disposition of mind be highly acceptable to that goddess to whose service you are dedicated, for her special characteristics are wisdom and foresight, and her very name seems to express the peculiar relation which she bears to knowledge. For "Isis" is a Greek word, and means "knowledge or wisdom,"(5) and "Typhon," (Set) the name of her professed adversary, is also a Greek word, and means " pride and insolence."(6) This latter name is well adapted to one who, full of ignorance and error, tears in pieces (7) and conceals that holy doctrine (about Asar) which the goddess collects, compiles, and delivers to those who aspire after the most perfect participation in the divine nature. This doctrine inculcates a steady perseverance in one uniform and temperate course of life (8),

and an abstinence from particular kinds of foods (9), as well as from all indulgence of the carnal appetite (10), and it restrains the intemperate and voluptuous part within due bounds, and at the same time habituates her votaries to undergo those austere and rigid ceremonies which their religion obliges them to observe. The end and aim of all these toils and labors is the attainment of the knowledge of the First and Chief Being (11), who alone is the object of the understanding of the mind; and this knowledge the goddess invites us to seek after, as being near and dwelling continually (12) with her. And this also is what the very name of her temple promiseth to us, that is to say, the knowledge and understanding of the eternal and self-existent Being - now it is called "Iseion," which suggests that if we approach the temple of the goddess rightly, we shall obtain the knowledge of that eternal and self existent Being."

Above: The Forms of Goddess Aset (Isis)

Mystical Implications of the Discourse of Plutarch:[56]

1- It is to be understood that spiritual aspiration implies seeking the union (Sema Tawi, mystical union-Yoga) with or becoming one with the thing being sought, because this is the only way to truly "know" partake of something. You can have opinions about what it is like to be a whale, but you would never exactly know until you become one with it, enfolding all that exists, is the one being worthy of veneration and identification. "Knowing" Neter (God) is the goal of all spiritual practices. This is the supreme goal, which must be kept in mind by a spiritual aspirant.

2- In order to discover the hidden nature of God, emphasis is placed on study and inquiry into the nature of things. Who am I? What is the universe composed of? Who is God? How am I related to God? These are the questions, which when pursued, lead to the discovery of the Self (God). Those who do not engage in this form of inquiry will generate a reality for themselves according to their beliefs. Some people believe they have the answers, that the universe is atoms and electrons or energy. Others believe that the body is the soul and that there is nothing else. Still others believe that the mind is the soul or that there is no soul and no God. The first qualification for serious aspiration is that you have a serious conviction that you are greater than just a finite individual mortal body, that you are an immortal being who is somehow mixed up with a temporal form (body). If this conviction is present, then you are stepping on the road to enlightenment. The teachings will be useful to you. Those who hold other beliefs are being led by ignorance and lack of spiritual sensitivity as a result of their beliefs. Thus, their beliefs will create a reality for them based on those beliefs. They will need to travel the road of nature, which will guide them in time toward the path of spiritual aspiration.

3-4 The plan prescribed by the teachings of Mystical spirituality (Sema Tawi – Yoga) is the only true means to effective spiritual development, because it leads to a revelation of the inner meanings of the teachings; therefore it is experiential, i.e., it is based on your own personal experience and not conjecture. Otherwise, worship and religious practices remain only at the level of ritualism and do not lead to enlightenment (Pert m Heru).

5-7 The Greek name Isis means "wisdom" which bestows the knowledge of the true Self of the initiate. In the Asarian (Osirian) Mysteries, when Set killed Asar by tearing him into pieces, he was symbolically tearing up the soul. However, Aset (Isis) restores the pieces of the soul (Asar). Set symbolizes egoism: pride, anger, hatred, fear, jealousy, etc. Therefore, pride and insolence (Set-egoism) destroy the soul and knowledge of the Self (Aset) restores it to its true nature. The Ancient Egyptian scriptures support the Greek name translation and meaning of the name Aset. One of the names of Aset is: *Rekhåt or Rekhit* ⟨hieroglyphs⟩ (meaning "knowledge personified"). *Rekh* is also a name of the God in the "duat" or Netherworld (astral plane) who possesses knowledge which can lead the soul to the abode of the Divine. The variation, *Rekh-t* ⟨hieroglyphs⟩, means Sage or learned person.

8- True spirituality cannot be pursued rashly or in a fanatical way by going to extremes. Sema Tawi, Mystical Spirituality, is a science of balance. It has been developed over a period of thousands of years with well established principles, which when followed, produce the desired effect of leading the initiate from darkness to light, ignorance to knowledge, an un-enlightened state to enlightenment.

9-10 The foods referred to are flesh foods (swine, sheep, fish, etc.), pulse,[57] and salt. Indulgence in sexual activity has two relevant aspects. First, it intensifies the physical experience of embodiment and distracts the mind by creating impressions in the subconscious and unconscious, which will produce future cravings and desires. This state of mind renders the individual incapable of concentration on significant worldly or high spiritual achievements. Secondly, control of the sexual urge leads to control of the sexual Life Force energy,[58] which can then be directed towards higher mental and spiritual achievement. Further, overindulgence in sexual activity tends to wear down the immunity as it wears down the mental capacity and one becomes a slave to sensual passions and susceptible to sexual and non-sex related diseases. The following verses from the Ancient Egyptian Book of Enlightenment show the practice of vegetarianism and celibacy.

Chapter 30B of the Ancient Egyptian mystical text *The Book of Coming Forth By Day (Book of the Dead)* states:

> *This utterance shall be recited by a person purified and washed; one who has not eaten animal flesh or fish.*

Chapter 64 of the *Book of Coming Forth By Day (Book of the Dead)* states:

> *This Chapter can be known by those who recite it and study it when they see no more, hear no more, have no more sexual intercourse and eat no meat or fish.*

Chapter 137A of the *Book of Coming Forth By Day (Book of the Dead)* states:

> *And behold, these things shall be performed by one who is clean, and is ceremonially pure, a man who hath eaten neither meat nor fish, and who hath not had intercourse with women* (applies to female initiates not having intercourse with men as well).

Images of The Basic Ancient Egyptian Postures

"Tjef Sema Paut Neteru"

For full descriptions of all postures see the book

EGYPTIAN YOGA: Postures of the Gods and Goddesses
By Muata Ashby

Kamitan Yoga Postures – from Ancient Egypt

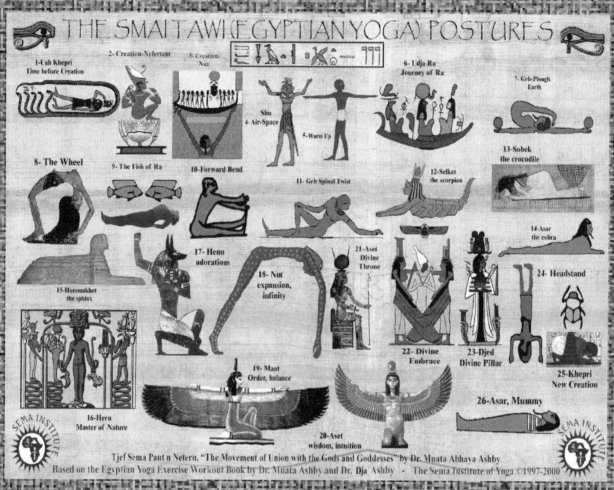

THE SMAI TAWI (EGYPTIAN YOGA) POSTURES

1-Uah Khepri Time before Creation
2- Creation-Nefertem
3- Creation-Nun
4-Air-Space Shu
5-Warm Up
6- Udja Ra Journey of Ra
7- Geb-Plough Earth
8- The Wheel
9- The Fish of Ra
10-Forward Bend
11- Geb Spinal Twist
12-Selket the scorpion
13-Sobek the crocodile
14-Asar the cobra
15-Horemakhet the sphinx
16-Heru Master of Nature
17- Henu adorations
18- Nut expansion, infinity
19- Maat Order, balance
20-Aset wisdom, intuition
21-Aset Divine Throne
22- Divine Embrace
23-Djed Divine Pillar
24- Headstand
25-Khepri New Creation
26-Asar, Mummy

Tjef Sema Paut n Netern, "The Movement of Union with the Gods and Goddesses" by Dr. Muata Abhaya Ashby
Based on the Egyptian Yoga Exercise Workout Book by Dr. Muata Ashby and Dr. Dja Ashby - The Sema Institute of Yoga ©1997-2000

Based on the Book

EGYPTIAN YOGA
Postures of the Gods and Goddesses
The Ancient Egyptian System of Physical Postures for Health, Meditation and Spiritual Enlightenment and the Ancient Egyptian Origins of Hatha Yoga
"Tjef Neteru   Sema Paut"

by
Dr. Muata Ashby and Dr. Karen "Dja" Ashby

Phase 1: Time Before Creation

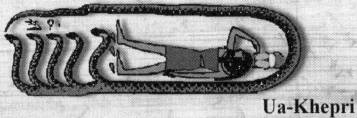

Ua-Khepri
Spirit Comes Into Being

From Valley of the Kings- Relief

The Lotus of Creation
and The Words of Power

From the Creation reliefs and varied

Nefertem

Nun: Primeval Waters

From: Sarcofagus of Seti I

Shu – Air, Space (Ether)

From the Creation Papyrus

The Geb Plough Posture

From: Temple of Hetheru

The Wheel Pose

From Relief

Sitting Forward Bend

From Tomb Relief

Geb - Spinal Twist

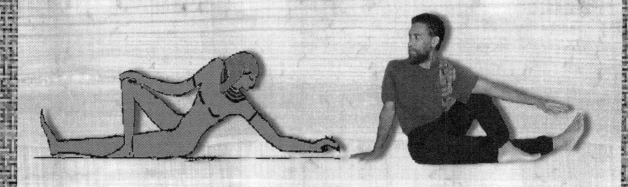

From Creation Papyrus

Selket: The Scorpion

From reliefs - based on Asarian Resurrection Myth

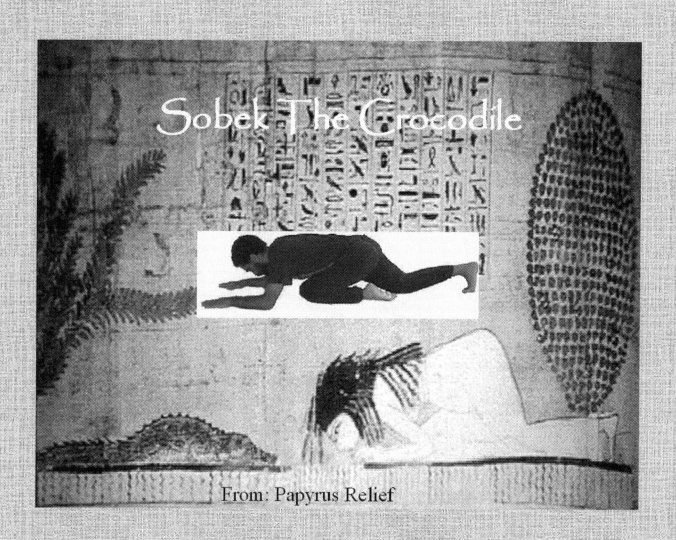

Sobek The Crocodile

From: Papyrus Relief

The Cobra Pose

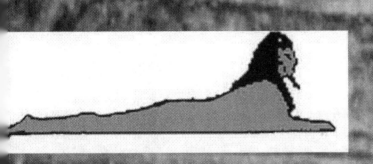

From: Temple of Hetheru

Maat: Righteousess, Order and Truth

Seen in many tomb reliefs and paintings

Nut: The Forward Bend

From: Various Temples, Tombs and
Papyrus Reliefs

Aset

Isis: The Heroic
Kneeling Pose

*Seen on reliefs and
statues*

ASET: The Divine Throne

On reliefs and Statues

ASET: The Divine Embrace

Seen on reliefs and statues

Asar: Djed
Establishment in the Higher Self

**From reliefs
and statues**

Head Stand
Turning reality upside down

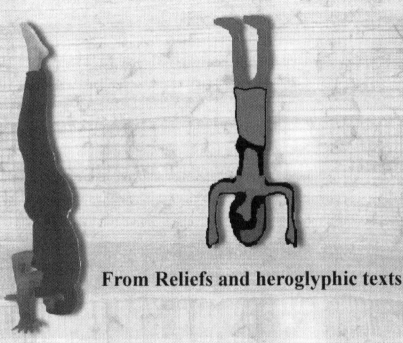

From Reliefs and heroglyphic texts

Khepri: The Scarab of Creation

From reliefs and hieroglyphic texts

Egyptian Yoga Postures at the Foot of the Step Pyramid in Sakkara Egypt, Africa

Below: Modern day practitioners of the Egyptian Yoga Postures at a Kamitan Temple Conference

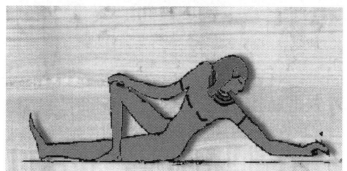

On reliefs and Statues

Below: Modern day practitioners of the Egyptian Yoga Postures at a Health Center

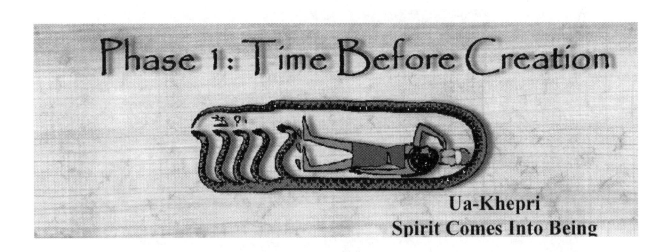

Ua-Khepri
Spirit Comes Into Being

Below: A Modern day Hatha Yoga Class in the West

Below: Modern day Hatha Yoga teacher practicing a Hatha Yoga posture at a Hindu Temple

Hatha Yoga as Caricature or as Commerce

The images below from advertisements around the United States of America, illustrate how Yoga practice in the West has been not only trivialized but attempts have been made to co-opt its message in order to twist it into areas of culture such as alcohol consumption that are diametrically opposed to the principles of yoga philosophy.

Above: Billboard on I-95 in Miami Florida for Absolute Vodka as Yoga practice.

Left: Legal services by a different kind of lawyers.

Below: Advertisements for exercise tank tops.

115

The System of Phases in the Practice of The Egyptian Yoga Postures

The Program of Thef Neteru Yoga differs from other forms of exercise (sports, recreation, games) in several important ways. First, it is a system for developing not only the physical aspect of a human being but also the mental and spiritual aspects as well. This occurs in the following way.

The practice of the physical postures of yoga affect not only the physical (outer) muscles (as ordinary exercises do) but also the nerves and the mind and thus develops the inner Life Force and Serpent Power energies, thereby awakening and cultivating the psychic energies of the Astral Body (body of life force and feelings-inner muscles) and the higher power of the inner self.

The understanding of the mythological teachings of the postures allows the practitioner to develop insight into the character and energy of each posture by understanding its presiding deity and enabling them to assume the role of that deity, thus allowing that cosmic force to be awakened within their consciousness. Therefore, along with the practice of the postures the practitioner should also study the mythology and teachings of the particular deity in order to gain insight into the feeling of the god or goddess of the posture. The gods and goddesses (Neteru) are in reality symbols of cosmic forces in nature and in the mind, which if understood and cultivated, cause a human being to develop their latent divine (Neteru) qualities, thus, engendering higher consciousness and spiritual enlightenment.

In Indian Hatha Yoga postures can be practiced in a prescribed sequence. That concept is called "vinyasa" in Indian practice. The practice of the postures should be seen as a journey of self-discovery and not as a chore or obligation simply to keep the physical body fit. That attitude will yield only limited results. The workout may be understood as a series of phases leading from Death to life, from before Creation to after Creation and from the Lower Self to the Higher.

The Beginning: Before Creation

In the beginning there were no forms, no Creation. There was only non-existence, but non-existence means absence of created objects (planets, stars, matter, the elements, etc.) and not absence of existence itself. The spirit was, is, and always will be and that spirit is symbolized by the Mummy (Karast) which is physically dead. The gods Asar and Anpu-Apuat preside over the dead mummy and from death life springs forth. This is the divine resurrection.

1- Karast (Mummy) Pose

Phase 1: Creation

As you perform the postures you will learn about and discover Creation. This is accomplished through the following poses.

2- Nefertem Lotus Pose

Nefertem is God in the form of the child, the innocence of creation as symbolized by the new born sun. He springs forth from the **Primeval Ocean** and sits atop the Lotus which is Creation itself, as its master. As God brought Creation into being through sound, or the word, which creates vibration or movement, so to the Journey of Enlightenment through the Thef Neteru (postures of the gods and goddesses) is begun with **Words Of Power** which set the proper vibrational tone to the environment, propitiate the presence of the cosmic forces to be discovered, harnessed and cultivated. If you have difficulty sitting in the lotus pose you may use the half lotus or the cross-legged posture.

WORDS OF POWER

In this practice the practitioner may use any words of power they were initiated into by their teacher or choose one from the spiritual texts.

3- Nun Pose.

Nun is the Primeval Ocean from which all creation arises. The aspirant should understand that Creation already existed as unformed matter before it came into being. Unformed matter was given form by ideas, will and sound of God. Nothing is Created, only transformed from already previously existing essence. God Creates using his very own essence just as a human being creates the dream world during a dream from their very own mental essence. This "essence of God" is also referred to as the Neteru (gods and goddesses or *cosmic forces*) emanating from Pa Neter (The Supreme Being).

Words of Power during the practice of individual postures.

A practitioner may also use words of power as you practice the individual postures. The Mysticism of the Neteru involves the task of discovering them within yourself. This is the most powerful and highest form of Yoga practice, seeing yourself as one with the divine. This means learning about the neteru, acting like them, talking like them, feeling like them and finally being them. This is the most important aspect of all Kemetic (Ancient Egyptian) ritual systems and it is so because of its power to transforms a human being. As you believe so you become. If you believe you are a lowly human being you will think, feel and act that way and your life will be a reflection of that limitation and degradation. If you understand you are more than that you will discover more, your true identity. This process is called yoga and the end or goal of this process is called spiritual enlightenment, resurrection. Therefore, as you practice the postures you should see yourself as embodying the principles of the presiding deity of that posture. This is why it is important to understand the myths related to each of the neteru.

Egyptian Yoga Exercise is more than physical exercise. It is a ritual system of **Forms and Special Movements for becoming Divine**, one with the gods and goddesses and ultimately discovering that these gods and goddesses or cosmic forces, are in reality emanations from your innermost self. Thus you may utter the words **"Nuk pu"** and the name of the presiding deity as you go into each posture. For example, as you enter the Aset pose say "Nuk pu Aset, Nuk pu Aset" and so forth.

4- Shu Pose

Shu represents space and air, which separates heaven and earth but which also sustains life. Therefore breathing in this and all exercises is very important.

Then you will discover how Creation is sustained.

5- Warm Up –Preparing to Sustain Creation. Warm up is very important before going into any posture so as not to hurt any muscles or tendons, etc.

You will discover how Creation is separated into heaven and earth. (**Nut and Geb**)

6- Journey of Ra Pose Series

The Journey of Ra Pose Series is actually a journey within the larger journey of the whole program. It means understanding the cycle of daily creation through which God sustains Creation at every moment. Creation is not just an event that occurred billions of years ago. It is an ongoing process. Every day you journey in the physical world through your mind and physical body and through the astral world when you dream at night. Your desire and will and your movement are what sustain your reality just as the constant movement of the spirit sustains Creation all the time. Coming into harmony with this means discovering the power to create a better life for yourself by taking control of your power in every moment of your life.

Phase 2: The Earth

Then you will discover the earth (gross-lower-physical nature) aspect of your own personality through the following postures.

7-8 Shoulder-stand Pose - Plough Pose,
9- Wheel Pose,
10- Fish Pose
11- Forward Bend Pose
12- Spinal Twist Pose

These poses primarily focus on the physical spine since it is the structure which allows the body to function. Flexibility of the spine means physical health and mental health. Constriction and calcification or weakness of the spine means pain and disease (physical and mental). These postures affect the mind because they promote the health and flexibility of the spinal nerves which in turn affect the mind, and the psycho-spiritual energy centers, which exist in the Astral Body.

Phase 3: Transition Poses

The transition poses assist a spiritual aspirant in moving from the Earth Series postures towards the Higher Self. Now that Creation has been engendered and sustained and the Earth aspect of life (gross) has been explored and glorified it is time to begin the journey of discovering the subtle aspect of life. The transition poses are:

13- Selket –Scorpion Pose
14- Sebek –Crocodile Pose
15– Arat- Cobra Pose
16- Horemacket –Sphinx Pose
17- Heru – Horus Pose and variations

Heru is the supreme defender of truth, righteousness and justice. He is the successful spiritual aspirant. Therefore, he represents virtue, honor and invincible will. He is the perfect balance between the higher and lower self and he therefore leads the spiritual aspirant into the inner shrine of the spirit, the Higher Self.

18– Henu Pose Series

The Henu Pose Series is optional in the general practice of the Thef Neteru System of psycho-spiritual exercises. However, it should be part of the advanced program of practice. The Henu Form is a series of postures performed to pay homage to the Divine. Its movements are slow and deliberate as well as graceful, creating a devotional feeling between practitioner and the Higher Self. Anpu, Heru, Set and others divinities preside over this posture and it is great honor to perform it.

Phase 4: The Higher Self Poses

The Higher Self is the subtle, expansive aspect of existence. It is presided over by the goddess in three special forms. Nut– expansive, infinite self. Maat– virtuous self. Aset– intuitional wisdom of self. Thus we have the following poses:

19- Nut Pose
20- Maat Pose and
21- Aset Winged Pose
22– Aset Sitting Pose
23-Aset Embrace Pose

Phase 5: Establishment Poses

The establishment poses are designed to help the practitioner become established in the benefits derived from the teachings and exercises of the previous phases. The Establishment Poses are:

24– Djed Pose
25- Headstand Pose
26- Khepri— Scarab Pose
27- Shti (Mummy) Pose

Shti means the body which is prepared for resurrection. This pose is used for the final relaxation and meditation of the session.

The Counter-Reversion Era, the Passing of Ancient Egyptian Religion into Dormancy, the Creation of Buddhism and the Formation of Western Religion

Above: Egyptian king at war with Asiatic invaders (wall relief). From a historical perspective it is interesting to note that the practice of Yoga Postures was in existence in Ancient Egypt but apparently nowhere else in the world until its emergence in India, after the contact between the Tantric Magical Buddhists and the Neterians at Menefer {Memphis} Egypt. However, we may also wonder at the occurrence of the emergence of Buddhism itself in the 6th century B.C.E. Specifically, why did it emerge at all? What was going on to necessitate its emergence? Also, the answers to these questions may reveal the reason why it was so compatible with Ancient Egyptian religion that its practitioners were allowed to establish a settlement in Memphis at all. Buddhism emerged in a period of history that may be termed "Counter-Reversion Era". It was a momentous time in human history in the ancient world wherein the old order of spiritual practice was in decline and the new order of barbarism was gaining unprecedented power in the ancient world, causing previously unknown levels of violence and disruption in societies in Asia and North Africa. A brief examination of this period in history will be useful to our study of the relationship between India, the Buddhists and the Ancient Egyptian religion.

Henotheism Period (10,000 B.C.E. – 550 B.C.E.)

The Ancient Egyptian religion was a purveyor of the perennial philosophy, the religious tradition of henotheism and panentheism that continued to be practiced openly until the 5th century A.C.E. [1,000 years later] when the Roman Orthodox Christians closed the last Egyptian temples by force.[59] Ancient Egypt had been the beacon of learning and science as well as spiritual wisdom. This is why the ancient pre-Judaic, pre-Christian and pre-Islamic religions had many areas of compatibility with Ancient Egyptian religion and some even included Ancient Egyptian gods and goddesses in their pantheon of divinities. The time prior to the *Counter-Reversion Era* was marked by the practice of henotheism {In philosophy and religion, is a term coined by Max Müller, which means devotion to a single god while accepting the existence of other gods.} and in a more developed format, pantheism {a doctrine identifying the Deity with the universe and its phenomena. Belief in and worship of all gods and goddesses as manifestations of the Supreme Being} and panentheism {the creator is Creation and transcends Creation}.

The Counter-Reversion Era (550 B.C.E.) Part 1:

During the sixth century B.C.E. there was a special age in human history, which some authors have termed "Axial age" due to its role in history that may be likened to an axis upon which many events turned. However, that period may be better described as a religious *"Counter-Reversion Era."* The name Counter-Reversion Era was chosen because it describes a time when the religious philosophy of the past [time before that era] was in decline due to the emergence of barbarism and certain religious movements emerged to counter that decline and revert back to the original *perennial philosophy*[60] of religion. During that time, there were several wars of conquest in which several nations in the Middle East developed into conquering forces. Some examples include the Persians and the Assyrians. That period marked a time when the power of Ancient Egypt, which had previously controlled the land areas from present day Sudan to India, at one time in the past, reached its lowest state. Ancient Egypt was under constant siege during that period. However, Egypt did not experience a religious *Counter-Reversion Era*

The *Counter-Reversion Era* covers a period circa the 6th century B.C.E. The philosophies that emerged at that time, such as Pythagoreanism, Buddhism, Jainism, Taoism, and Confucianism had common aspects that hearkened back to and admonished the need to return to a philosophy of mystical spirituality, community service and ethics, such as was taught by the Ancient Egyptians for several thousands of years. Those philosophies, except in Greece, developed in a personalized form, with a personal leader in he form of a realized and or ascended master at its center, as opposed to the priestly format of Ancient Egypt. In other words, the degradation of humanity in the Middle East, due to strife, caused a desire for spirituality that was more personality based instead of mystically based. Ancient Egyptian religion was originally personality based [Ex. God Ra, Osiris or Isis]; however, those personalities did not interfere with the capacity for the practitioners to attain high religious development since the systems introduced by those personalities were based on mystical philosophy with henotheistic components. Therefore, even though the religions that came in during the *Counter-Reversion Era* had specific founding teachers [personalities upon which the religions were based: *Pythagoras, Buddha, Mahavira, Lao-Tzu, Confucius*], their philosophies pointed to mysticism and the perennial philosophy that has existed before and led people to turn away from violence and towards cooperative peaceful coexistence and a personal quest for enlightenment by discovering the nature of self which transcends the phenomenal and which is essentially a part of the immortal, transcendental Divine, concepts that predated the inception of these new religions and philosophies.

Chaos in Ancient Egypt and the Creation of New World Religions including Buddhism Part 2

There was an important development in the 6th century B.C.E. that occurred in Egypt at the time when Buddhism emerged. It may be termed "Counter-Reversion Era" since the new religions were trying to counter the chaos caused by barbarian cultures which were disrupting the previous age-old form of spirituality that had persisted previously for thousands of years. Prior to this era Ancient Egypt had been the Holy Land for many peoples; they looked up to Ancient Egypt and a paragon of religious wisdom and spiritual practice. However, that was changing due to the invasions that brought chaos to Egypt and much of the ancient world.

Cambyses II (reigned 529-522 BC), the king of Persia, led an expedition to conquer Egypt, which at the time was the sole independent kingdom in the aftermath the conquests of Asia by his father. Cambyses defeated Psamtik III, king of Egypt, and succeeded in conquering Egypt as far south as Nubia, but he failed in later attacks on the Egyptian oasis of Ammonium (now Siwa) and in campaigns in Ethiopia.

The attacks and conquest of Egypt by the Persians caused an extensive displacements of the Egyptian population. It was at this time that some of the Priests and Priestesses were forced out of the Temples due to fires set by the armies of the Persians. Also, many Egyptians were forcibly taken as slave workers to Persia and other parts of Asia Minor to build monuments and Temples for the Persians in those areas.[61][62] It is during this time that the most powerful and influential philosophies of the ancient world came into being. These included:

- Buddhism   6th century B.C.E.
- Pythagoreanism   6th century B.C.E.
- Taoism   6th century B.C.E.
- Confucianism   6th century B.C.E.
- Zoroastrianism   6th century B.C.E.
- Jainism   6th century B.C.E.

The Ancient Egyptians had been attacked and the country taken over by foreigners twice before. The first time was the Hyksos invasion, which precipitated the "Second Intermediate Period," and the second time was the invasion of the Assyrians which was put down by the Nubians. However, the records indicate[63] that the viciousness of the attack and conquest by the Persians was so severe that it prompted a migration of Ancient Egyptians not only to Asia Minor, but also to India, Europe and other parts of Africa, including Nubia to the south, and West Africa also. Therefore, a causal connection can be drawn between the events in Egypt and the events in other parts of the ancient world. The surviving culture of Egypt was severely weakened after the Persian conquest, so much so that after a brief reestablishment of Egyptian rule by Egyptians, they were conquered again by the Greeks, who themselves had conquered the Persians. This period brought some stability to Egypt as the Greeks allowed the Ancient Egyptian religion to continue under their auspices, and the connection that had been established between other countries and Egypt through the Egyptians that had migrated out of Egypt 200 years earlier[64] during the invasion of Cambyses and the open relations fostered by the Ptolemaic rulers continued into a new phase. Now Egypt was fully opened to the spiritual seekers of the ancient world, and they flocked to the land of the Pyramids.

In this respect some researchers have noted the similarities between the Ancient Egyptian and Buddhist iconographies and point to these, and the evidences of philosophical correlations and evidences of contact along with the images of Buddha himself, as sufficient proof to show that Buddha was an African-Egyptian priest. Indeed, even when we consider that no images of Buddha were allowed until the 1st century B.C.E. with the advent of Mahayana Buddhism, the images that appear even at that time, and later, up to the present day, bear a resemblance to the Kamitan-Kushitic forms of imagery and human appearance. There is a resemblance especially in the depiction of the hair and certain aspects of the physiognomy, in particular the nose and eye region of the face. The hair is curly or in locks, a form that was originated in ancient Kamit.

The Assurance Age

Judaism was practiced in ancient times to the extent that the Torah [the main original Jewish religious texts] is believed by scholars to have been read publicly since the time of Ezra (c. 450 B.C.E. –after the *Counter-Reversion Era*).[65] However, at that time, Judaism did not have the

Rabbinical Jewish principles of absolute monotheism as we may understand its practice today which rejects all gods and recognizes only one. At this time Judaism accepted the henotheistic concept which means devotion to a single god while accepting the existence of other gods. This was especially true of Egyptian Jews who developed Judaism and the Septuagint in Alexandria. However, after the Babylonian conquest of Jerusalem, the Jews (people of Judah, part of the land ruled by the kings Saul, David, Solomon and their descendants)[66] scattered to Egypt and to Babylonia. It seems also contradictory that the Jews who practice the Passover ritual and who commemorate being freed from captivity in Egypt should seek refuge in that same country. Nevertheless, the Egyptian Jews continued to practice the earlier form of Judaism but the Babylonian Jews started to innovate the philosophical tenets of Judaism as a reaction to the debacle caused by the Babylonian destruction of Jerusalem and the Jewish Temple in 586 B.C.E.[67] It is possible that the Babylonian Jews could have come into contact with practitioners of the Zoroastrian tradition at that time. The Babylonian exile period began to set in motion changes in Jewish religion that came to fruition in the next pivotal period of religion in the Middle East that was to have far reaching effects on Christianity and the rest of Western culture in the first and second millenniums A.C.E. which may be termed Assurance Age. This Assurance Age was marked by a turn away from Henotheism and the Counter-reversion era religions and the adoption of orthodox, dogmatic religions that emphasized faith-based practice instead of absolute monotheism, historicity, literalism and apocalyptcism in religious practice. That form of religion was and continues to be prone to fanaticism since faith based religions must necessarily be at odds with any tradition that does not agree with its tenets.

Conclusion

This study was undertaken due to an initial recognition of basic similarities between Ancient Egyptian and Indian cultural factors. This initially conjectural study transformed into a theory based on mounting evidence and later into a thesis[68] in order to discover if the evidence supported the hypothesis.[69] Also, this study was undertaken to assist in the rediscovery of Kamitan culture, philosophy and religion. The idea was that if Hindu culture is a continuation of a larger culture which once encompassed north-east Africa and southern Asia, then it might be possible to understand Ancient Egyptian mysticism and religion from the perspective of a living instead of dead culture. It would then be possible to understand the mysteries of Ancient Egypt as an original source for many of the most fundamental teachings surviving not just in Hinduism, but also Ancient Greek Philosophy, Judaism and Christianity. Thus, the research has turned out to be like tracing back to the source, like discovering the seed from which a plant has grown. In knowing the seed it is possible to know the plant (spirituality) and its branches (the religions) better and vise versa, thereby illuminating them in modern times with the depth of their own deeper history which leads back to the place where all life and civilization was born.

The work at the Sema Institute of Yoga has shown that the origins of mystical religion and Yoga run much deeper than previously understood and appear to lead to Africa, but this need not be a threatening notion. It should be accepted as a wonderful example of the commonality of human consciousness which is acknowledged universally by geneticists and anthropologists as having emerged in Africa. Even though modern Buddhism cannot be said to be exactly the same practice as what was being done by the Ancient Egyptian priests and priestesses, it is a wondrous realization that Ancient Egyptian religion did not die but still lives on in some fashion, in its adherents who follow the Kamitan path of spirituality, and those who follow Gnosticism, Hinduism, Buddhism and Yoga as it developed in India, for these two lands are verily like mother and daughter. The mother nurtured and loved the daughter and when it came time for the mother to pass on, the daughter carried on the traditions of mystical life for generations to come. Therefore, Ancient Egypt and India may be considered to be the caretakers of the same mystical tradition and the oldest living culture, civilization and spiritual tradition, since when considered together, the span of time encompassed by Ancient Egypt and India, as one established successive culture, span well beyond the duration of any other known culture or civilization.

It must be borne in mind that cultural adoptions and adaptations are as organic in cultural relationships as in human relationships. Human beings are affected by everything they are exposed to in some degree, language difficulties not withstanding. Further, those who are at the forefront in leadership in the task of carrying on a tradition should realize that they too are in effect adopting a culture, for the teaching as it was given by the sages in Ancient Egypt or India thousands of years ago related to the social needs of those times. Therefore, we too are adopting and adapting the culture of mystical spirituality, wherein time and space are ultimately discarded in favor of absolute truth. Otherwise, what remains are dates and times, concepts and histories, myths and symbols, culture and limitation. Thus, our adoption must remain true to the principles of the teaching but also realistically face the oftentimes incongruous puzzle of the world and make sense of it in a way that promotes peace and enlightenment that is in keeping with the vision or spirit of the tradition.

The fear of seeing unity is actually the fear that keeps humanity bound to the cycle of violence, war and disease as individual human beings as well as whole cultures. As a garden with many flowers produces a beautiful scenery, even with the differences, a culture must learn to see itself as one among a family of cultures that comprise the garden religions and spiritual traditions. The fragrance of the flower of spiritual traditions manifests as the myriad of human mythologies. This problem of fear is not just the province of "the ignorant masses," but it is unfortunately the mainstay among many intellectuals and "well"-educated leaders of society. This problem exists even within those ranks of yoga practitioners who find it easy to espouse the universality of yoga as long as it is said from the perspective of "yoga originated in India." The question is how can the true goals of yoga, the attainment of universal vision, be achieved by yoga practitioners and pundits with such attitudes of nationalism, pride and proprietorship over yoga? Why is the ownership of yoga so important? If Creation is infinite and God is infinite and the world, cultures and mythologies are transient, how can any society make a claim on anything but being part of a stream of spiritual consciousness which is manifest in universal myth? All human beings have built what they have, standing upon the shoulders of their forefathers and foremothers. Therefore, all culture and civilization is due to a long-standing relation to the past, going back ultimately to the beginning, and the Creator. This self-evident reality denigrates no one and exalts no one, but rather shows everyone's place in time and space and history as well as the evolution of the search for self-knowledge, the coveted goal of Divine consciousness, through religious and mystical philosophy which is the single common factor uniting all human beings from the beginning of time.

We cannot live together with bias against each other, some saying that the East is best, others the West, and so on. What about the south, the very cradle of humanity itself? Africa and its pinnacle of culture in ancient times was unquestionably a major force in shaping humanity, but the nature of this force has been forgotten or misunderstood, or simply relegated to commercialism, as a vacation destination, or even a curiosity. But what about the glory, the art, the philosophy and the legacy of the spirituality of Ancient Kamit?

This book does not purport to give the idea that Ancient Egypt (Kamit) is the be all and end all of humanity, culture, civilization, etc., since there was certainly a deeper origin than that (from Pre-Kamitan- Ancient African Religion, Culture and Philosophy that gave rise to Kamitan Culture and Spirituality). However, what the Ancient Africans in Kamit achieved is so meritorious and of such great import in its potential contribution to the storehouse of human knowledge and understanding that its rightful place among the major factors in human development must be acknowledged and realized. If this is done it is my firm belief that the community of nations will move one giant step closer to conviviality and peace as well as collective spiritual enlightenment.

The evidences presented in this volume show that there was a strong relation between Ancient Egypt and India and that this relationship allowed the perpetuation of a mystical tradition which is today called Yoga and mysticism. Mysticism is that art of allowing oneself to be transformed, to discover one's higher identity as one with that Transcendental essence. The particular "style" of mysticism in Ancient Egypt and India has been found to match in the basic fundamentals as well as in peripheral aspects. Thus, it is in a way gratifying to see that the glory that was Ancient Egypt still lives on in India.

While it is true that yoga in its universal sense transcends communities and social structures as well as ethnic boundaries, the time and space (practical) reality of human existence requires a pragmatic approach when dealing with human beings who have not evolved into higher consciousness and who still subscribe to concepts of race or class issues. While we may transcend to higher levels of consciousness through the practice of mysticism and Yoga, we also exist on the physical plane and interact with others through the medium of physical bodies which operate and relate by means of culture. This means that our efforts towards community upliftment are ultimately related to cultural upliftment as well.

Many people have been purchasing the books from the Egyptian Yoga book series over the years but were surprised to find out that there existed disciplines of meditation and yogic postures in Ancient Africa prior to their development in India. The surprise really manifested when the workshops and lectures were held. People actually experienced for themselves the disciplines and were shown the original scriptures which provide the instruction and the point was brought home in a very powerful way. They were surprised to find that while similar, the disciplines are actually independent and more ancient and thus entirely African.

Another growing issue is that communities of African descent in the U.K., like those in other countries such as Guyana, Kenya, Trinidad and elsewhere, have developed hostility with the Indian community due to the Indian cohesiveness and systematic exclusion of people of African descent from their social, economic and political structures. Thus, due to the history of the caste system in India, suffering under British racism and colonialism, a developing self-centered national cultural ego has emerged in the Indian community, and due to widespread ignorance in the Indian community about the origins of their own culture, there is a growing rift between Indians and Africans. This point became so well-known in recent years that a major Hollywood motion picture was dedicated to the subject (*Mississippi Masalla* - {1992}). In recent years, perhaps beginning with the Apartheid and Western racist practices which conform in many respects to the caste system of India (which has been denounced by every authentic Indian spiritual leader), many Indians have become culturally conceited and openly repudiate peoples of African descent. In a sense this may be because, like an ordinary person repudiates those who remind him/her of {his/her} own degradation, Indian peoples have recently also emerged from the scourge of slavery. Although they did not suffer the decimation of their population and complete disruption of their culture, Indians do carry the scars of victimization by foreign powers including the Greeks, Arabs and British among others. When they see peoples of African descent they may be reminded of their own inadequacies and suffering as well as humiliation as they continue to observe peoples of African descent, who still even to this day find themselves caught in the mire of ignorance, disorganization and discontent. Authentic Hindu spiritual masters would never advocate racism towards any group nor would they permit their followers to engage in economic monopolies to exclude or subjugate others. Therefore, it must be understood that those people who consider themselves as Hindus but who are engaging in such negative practices are not doing so under the auspices of their authentic spiritual leaders, but rather following the instructions of community leaders who are dedicated to the ends of greed, based on the concepts of segregation and subjugation of peoples who they consider to be of a lower caste, i.e. the dark skinned South Indians and of course also the dark skinned peoples of African descent. Again, just as in every other culture, most Indians do not study the philosophy of their own heritage, but are rather content to perform rituals and praise their spiritual scriptures without studying them under the direction of qualified spiritual preceptors. This error opens the door to misinterpretation and also misunderstanding of the teachings, leading to cultural egocentricity, even to the extent of remaking the scriptures in their own image, to suit their needs or desires, or simply ignoring the injunctions of the spiritual teachings and following them in name only, for many Hindus love and accept worship services and enjoy singing and praising the Divine, but are inept and some even completely ignorant as to how to apply the teaching in their own lives within their own culture, let alone outside of it.

In the U.S., many people of African descent resent Indians and also believe Yoga originated in India, and that it is an Eastern and therefore "alien" practice. This occurs for many reasons. One is that Indian culture, generally speaking, is not in harmony with their own authentic practices within the mystical Indian Yoga tradition. Another may be opinions drawn from previous interactions with Indians. Another reason is that being in the West, most people follow Christianity in some form, and this system admonishes them to stay away from any "non-Christian" religions and cultures. Yet another may be that their karmic experiences dictate a different spiritual path for them in this life time and therefore, Indian Spirituality will be inherently unappealing. Karmicly, they cannot approach it because it does not "belong" to their culture. Thus, the already preexisting misconceptions that "Yoga" originated or only existed in India and that Indian Culture was a separate development from the African are further compounded by the economic and political wranglings. The misconceptions on both sides need to be addressed by the spiritual leaders of each group. However, the voice of knowledge seldom finds the ear of the ego, especially when the voice is weak and lack of purity is a source of weakness.

In view of the growing search for roots and self-knowledge, many people of African descent (including Yoga teachers) who have come into contact with the book *Egyptian Yoga* and the Egyptian Yoga Book Series have been pleasantly surprised and also gratified to find out about the African origins, which for many of them actually confirms much of what they already suspected based on limited research. These are perhaps some issues we may reflect upon in the light of the findings in this book. However, it is not sufficient to be able to have this book and point to it as a resource. Those practitioners who may want to promote it should do so best by practicing the Ancient Egyptian teaching and educating their students and others of the deeper history of Hatha Yoga in the Kamitan Sema Paut system of physical postures. Otherwise the mere lip service, just stating that Yoga originates in Egypt or Africa will have less power. It would have less power also if it is simply stated by Yoga teachers but then they proceed to practice only Indian derived postures and not the Kamitan ones.

NOTES and REFERENCES

[1] *In Search of the Cradle of Civilization,* 1995, p. 15, co-authored by Georg Feuerstein, David Frawley, and Subhash Kak.

[2] Ancient Indian scriptural written language

[3] *The RIG VEDA* Ralph T.H. Griffith, translator 1889

[4] Yoga Journal, {The New Yoga} January/February 2000

[5] Yoga International, {The Flight of the Alone to the Alone}, November 2000

[6] major temple and city in Ancient Egypt.

[7] See previous note.

[8] See previous note.

[9] Yoga Journal, {The New Yoga} January/February 2000

[10] *Living Yoga,* Georg Feuerstein, Stephan Bodian, with the staff of Yoga Journal

[11] Note: also see the section on Serpent Power further on in this chapter for more in depth and expanded details

[12] *A Sanskrit-English Dictionary,* Monier Williams, p. 528

[13] For a summary of the argument and a bibliography on this subject see Mircea Eliade, *Yoga: Immortality and Freedom,* Bollingen Series LVI, 2nd edn. (Princeton: Princeton University Press, 1969), PP. 370-372 ("Patanjali and the Texts of Classic Yoga").

[14] *The Mythic Image,* Joseph Campbell

[15] See the section of this book entitled *The Serpent Power Philosophy and Iconography.* For more details on the Kamitan Serpent Power Yoga system see the book *The Serpent Power,* by Muata Ashby

[16] *Sports and Games of Ancient Egypt* by Wolfgang Decker

[17] Commonly referred to as Chapter 17

[18] Commonly referred to as Chapter 176

[19] Feuerstein, Georg. (1996). *The Shambhala Guide to Yoga.* Boston & London: Shambhala Publications, Inc.

[20] Random House Encyclopedia Copyright (C) 1983,1990

[21] Doshi, Saryu, Editor-Indian Council for Cultural Relations India and Egypt: Influences and Interactions 1993

[22] *Pottery Headrests from Narsipur Sangam,* F.R. Allchin, *Studies in Indian Prehistory,* D. Sen and A.K. Ghosh, eds., Calcutta, 1966, pp. 58-63

[23] *Chanudaro Excavations, 1935-36* E.J.H. Mackay, American Oriental Society, New Heaven, 19443, pp. 25 and 220, pl. XCII, 38

[24] Nagaraja Rao, op. Cit., p. 144; also Allchin, op. Cit.

[25] Ibid.

[26] Rashidi, Runoko and Van Sertima, Ivan, Editors *African Presence in Early Asia 1985-1995*

[27] Doshi, Saryu, Editor-Indian Council for Cultural Relations *India and Egypt: Influences and Interactions* 1993

[28] *Mansouri El S. M., Art – Culture of India and Egypt 1959*

[29] *From Fetish to God in Ancient Egypt* by E.W. Budge

[30] The term magic is not used in the western sense. Here it means disciplines of transformative power through sound, posture and ritual.

[31] vinyasa (sequences of poses synchronized with the breath)

[32] Wikipedia Encyclopedia

[33] http://www.gotquestions.org/Christian-yoga.html

[34] http://www.religionnewsblog.com/12332

[35] http://www.acfnewsource.org/religion/christian_yoga.html

[36] http://www.briomag.com/briomagazine/briobeyond/a0004643.html

[37] Wikipedia encyclopedia http://en.wikipedia.org/wiki/Yoga_piracy

[38] For a more detailed study see the book **The Serpent Power** – by Dr. Muata Ashby

[39] Late Ancient Egyptian motif.

[40] Dictionary of Ancient Egypt. Ian Shaw and Paul Nicholson

[41] Kundalini, Ajit Mookergee

[42] ibid

[43] ibid

[44] *The Tantric Way* by Ajit Mookerjee and Madhu Khanna

[45] *Sexual Life in Ancient Egypt* by Lise Manniche

[46] For more details see the book **Egyptian Yoga Volume 1**

[47] For more details see the book **Egyptian Yoga Volume 1**

[48] Constructed in the period of the Indian King Asoka (Ashoka) who adopted Buddhism.

[49] African Religion Vol. 3 Memphite Theology.

[50] American Heritage Dictionary

[51] This category includes fish, and eggs. (*The Sivananda Companion to Yoga,* Lucy Lidell, Narayani, Giris Rabinovitch)

[52] This category includes meat, and alcohol. (The Sivananda Companion to Yoga)

[53] Discipline of reaching enlightenment by means of a dualistic thought process for understanding the Self from not-Self. It developed contemporaneously with the Yoga – Bhagavad Gita tradition.

[54] Bhagavad Gita Chapter 2 Samkhya Yogah--The Yoga of Knowledge by Swami Jyotirmayananda

[55] *Porphyry,* On Abstinence from Killing Animals, trans. Gillian Clark (Ithaak, 1999). (= *De abstentia,* Book IV, chap 6)

[56] Note: The numbers at the beginning of each paragraph below correspond to the reference numbers in the text above.

[57] **pulse** (pŭls) *n.* **1.** The edible seeds of certain pod-bearing plants, such as peas and beans. **2.** A plant yielding these seeds. (American Heritage Dictionary)

[58] The concept of the Life Force will be explained in detail later.

[59] *African Origins of Civilization,* by Muata Ashby, *Mystical Journey From Jesus to Christ,* by Muata Ashby

60 The Perennial Philosophy (Latin philosophia perennis) is the idea that a universal set of truths common to all people and cultures exists. The term was first used by the German mathematician and philosopher Gottfried Leibniz to designate the common, eternal philosophy that underlies all religious movements, in particular the mystical streams within them. The term was later popularized by Aldous Huxley in his 1945 book The Perennial Philosophy. The term "perennial philosophy" has also been used to translate the concept of the "eternal or perennial truth" in the Sanskrit Sanatana Dharma.

The concept of perennial philosophy is the fundamental tenet of the Traditionalist School, formalized in the writings of 20th century metaphysicians René Guénon and Frithjof Schuon. The Indian scholar and writer Ananda Coomaraswamy, associated with the Traditionalists, also wrote extensively about the perennial philosophy.

http://en.wikipedia.org/wiki/Perennial_philosophy

[61] Cambyses II (d. 522 BC), son of Cyrus the Great and King of Persia (529-522 BC), his main achievement was the conquest of Egypt. His other campaigns failed and turned him from a benevolent to a harsh ruler. He died in battle in Syria. (Random House Encyclopedia Copyright (C) 1983,1990)

[62] *The African Origins of Civilization,* Cheikh Anta Diop, 1974

[63] *History of Herodotus, Reliefs on the palace of Ashurbanipal*

[64] Review section entitled ***Paleoanthropology shows a connection between Ancient Egypt, Ancient Persia and Ancient India***

65 Essential Judiasm: A Complete Guide to Beliefs, Customs and Rituals by George Robinson (Pocket Books, 2000). "Torah, Torah, Torah: The Unfolding of a Tradition." Judaism for Dummies (Hungry Minds, 2001). Tracey R. Rich, "Torah." Judaism 101 (1995-99).

66 While the term Jewish is used largely as a religious or and ethnic designation it is actually a religious designation or name.

67 Jewish Life in Ancient Egypt by Edward Bleiberg for the Brooklyn Museum 2002

[68] **the·sis** (thē′sĭs) *n., pl.* **the·ses** (-sēz). **1.** A proposition that is maintained by argument.

[69] **hy·poth·e·sis** (hī-pŏth′ĭ-sĭs) *n., pl.* **hy·poth·e·ses** (-sēz′). *Abbr.* **hyp.**, **hypoth. 1.** A tentative explanation that accounts for a set of facts and can be tested by further investigation; a theory.

Bibliography

1. A Concise Encyclopedia of Hinduism, by Klaus K. Klostermaier
2. A Concise History of Buddhism by Andrew Skilton
3. A Sanskrit-English Dictionary, Monier Williams, p. 528
4. African Presence in Early Asia edited by Ivan Van Sertima and Runoko Rashidi
5. African Origins of Civilization by Muata Ashby
6. Am I a Hindu?: the Hinduism Primer by Ed. Viswanathan
7. Art - Culture of India and Egypt, the author S. M El Mansouri
8. Bardo Teachings by Lama Lodo
9. Based on the new discoveries at the city of Mehrgarh - Indus Valley
10. Buddha: the Intelligent Heart by Alistair Shearer
11. Buddha: the Intelligent Heart" by Alistair Shearer
12. Charles Elliot, Hinduism and Buddhism, vol. III, London, 1954, pp. 93-94
13. Civilizations of the Indus Valley and Beyond, Sir Mortimer Wheeler.
14. Comparative Mythology, Jaan Puhvel
15. Connection of Egypt with India, F.W.H. Migeod, Man, vol. 24, no. 118, London, 1924, p. 160
16. Dancing Wu Li Masters by Gary Zukov
17. Dangerous Friend: A Teacher-Student Relationship in Vajrayana Buddhism by Rig'dzin Dorje
18. Death, Intermediate State and Rebirth in Tibetan Buddhism by Lati Rinbochay & Jeffrey Hopkins
19. Decline and Fall of Buddhism by Dr. K. Jamanadas
20. Doshi, Saryu, Editor-Indian Council for Cultural Relations India and Egypt: Influences and Interactions 1993
21. Dutta, P. C. 1984. Biological anthropology of Bronze Ace. Harappans: new perspectives. In The People of South Asia.
22. Egypt and India by Muata Ashby
23. Egyptian Yoga Postures of the Gods and Goddesses by Muata Ashby
24. Eliade, Yoga: Immortality and Freedom, Bollingen Series LVI, 2nd edn. (Princeton: Princeton University Press, 1969), PP. 370-372 ("Patanjali and the Texts of Classic Yoga").
25. Encyclopedia of Mysticism and Mystery Religions by John Ferguson
26. Encyclopedic Dictionary of Yoga by Georg Feurstein
27. Encyclopedic Dictionary of Yoga" by Georg Feurstein
28. Ferdmand's Handbook to the World's Religions
29. Feuerstein, Georg, The Shambhala Encyclopedia of Yoga 1997
30. Gods of India, p. 35. Martin
31. H. G. Rawlinson, Intercourse between India and the Western World, Cambridge
32. Hatha-Yoga-Pradipika, The Shambhala Encyclopedia of Yoga by Georg Feuerstein, Ph. D.
33. Hatha Yoga The Hidden Language by Swami Sivananda Radha
34. Hindu Myths by Wendy O'Flaherty

35. Hindu Myths" by Wendy O'Flaherty
36. In Search of the Cradle of Civilization, 1995, co-authored by Georg Feuerstein, David Frawley, and Subhash Kak.
37. Indian Myth and Legend, Donald A. Mckenzie
38. Indian Mythology, Veronica Ions
39. Integral Yoga by Swami Jyotirmayananda
40. International Society for Krishna Consciousness
41. J.C.Harke, "The Indian Terracottas from Ancient Memphis: Are they really Indian?, Dr. Debala Mitra Volume, Delhi, 1991, pp. 55-61
42. Jnana Yoga by Swami Jyotirmayananda
43. Jnana Yoga" by Swami Jyotirmayananda
44. K. G. Krishnan, Uttankita Sanskrit Vidya Arangnya Epigraphs, vol. II, Mysore, 1989, pp 42 ff
45. Kosambi, D. D., Ancient India a History of its Culture and Civilisation, 1965.
46. Kundalini by Gopi Krishna
47. Kundalini" by Gopi Krishna
48. Living Yoga, Georg Feuerstein, Stephan Bodian, with the staff of Yoga Journal
49. Macdonell, A. A., Vedic Mythology, Delhi: Motilal Banarsidass, 1974.
50. Mackenzie, Donald A., Indian Myth and Legend, London 1913
51. Mansouri El S. M., Art - Culture of India and Egypt 1959
52. Monier-Williams, Indian Wisdom, p. 19.
53. Mystical spirituality texts of India.
54. Mysticism of Hindu Gods and Goddesses by Swami Jyotirmayananda
55. Mysticism of the Mahabharata Swami Jyotirmayananda 1993
56. Pottery Headrests from Narsipur Sangam, F.R. Allchin, Studies in Indian Prehistory, D. Sen and A.K. Ghosh, eds., Calcutta, 1966, pp. 58-63
57. Prehistoric India and Ancient Egypt 1956 Ray, Kumar Sudhansu
58. Proof of Vedic Culture's Global Existence by Steven Knapp
59. Raja Yoga Sutras, Swami Jyotirmayananda
60. Rashidi, Runoko and Van Sertima, Ivan, Editors African Presence in Early Asia 1985-1995
61. Ray, Kumar Sudhansu, Prehistoric India and Ancient Egypt 1956
62. Reading Buddhist Art by Meher McArthur
63. Rig Veda by Aryan and Indian Sages
64. SADHANA by Swami Sivananda
65. SADHANA" by Swami Sivananda
66. Sanskrit Keys to the Wisdom Religion, by Judith Tyberg
67. Search for the Buddha by Charles Allen
68. The Bhagavad Gita" translated by Antonio DE Nicola
69. The Bhagavad Gita" translated by Swami Jyotirmayananda
70. The Great Book of Tantra" by Indra Sinha
71. The Living Gita by Swami Satchidananda 3rd ed. 1997
72. The RIG VEDA Ralph T.H. Griffith, translator 1889
73. The Sivananda Companion to Yoga, Lucy Lidell, Narayani, Giris Rabinovitch)
74. The Story of Buddhism by Donald S. Lopez Jr.
75. The Story of Islam
76. The Tantric Way by Ajit Mookerjee and Madhu Khanna

77. The Tantric Way" by Ajit Mookerjee and Madhu Khanna
78. The Tao of Physics, Fritjof Capra
79. The Tibetan Book of the Dead by Francesca Fremantle & Chogyam Trungpa
80. The Upanishads, Max Muller, translator
81. The Upanishads: Breath of the Eternal, Swami Prabhavananda and Frederick Manchester
82. The Upanishads" by Swami Prabhavananda
83. The Yoga of Wisdom, Swami Jyotirmayananda
84. Vedic Aryans and the Origins of Civilization by David Frawley
85. Vivekacudamani" by Shankaracarya
86. Way of Tibetan Buddhism by Lama Jampa Thaye
87. Yoga Vasistha Ramayana translated by Swami Jyotirmayananda
88. Yoga Vasistha Vol. I by Sage Valmiki -Translation by Swami Jyotirmayananda
89. Yoga Vasistha, Nirvana Prakarana Swami Jyotirmayananda, 1998

Index

Other Books From C M Books

P.O.Box 570459
Miami, Florida, 33257
(305) 378-6253 Fax: (305) 378-6253

This book is part of a series on the study and practice of Ancient Egyptian Yoga and Mystical Spirituality based on the writings of Dr. Muata Abhaya Ashby. They are also part of the Egyptian Yoga Course provided by the Sema Institute of Yoga. Below you will find a listing of the other books in this series. For more information send for the Egyptian Yoga Book-Audio-Video Catalog or the Egyptian Yoga Course Catalog.

Now you can study the teachings of Egyptian and Indian Yoga wisdom and Spirituality with the Egyptian Yoga Mystical Spirituality Series. The Egyptian Yoga Series takes you through the Initiation process and lead you to understand the mysteries of the soul and the Divine and to attain the highest goal of life: ENLIGHTENMENT. The *Egyptian Yoga Series*, takes you on an in depth study of Ancient Egyptian mythology and their inner mystical meaning. Each Book is prepared for the serious student of the mystical sciences and provides a study of the teachings along with exercises, assignments and projects to make the teachings understood and effective in real life. The Series is part of the Egyptian Yoga course but may be purchased even if you are not taking the course. The series is ideal for study groups.

Prices subject to change.

1.   EGYPTIAN YOGA: THE PHILOSOPHY OF ENLIGHTENMENT An original, fully illustrated work, including hieroglyphs, detailing the meaning of the Egyptian mysteries, tantric yoga, psycho-spiritual and physical exercises. Egyptian Yoga is a guide to the practice of the highest spiritual philosophy which leads to absolute freedom from human misery and to immortality. It is well known by scholars that Egyptian philosophy is the basis of Western and Middle Eastern religious philosophies such as *Christianity, Islam, Judaism,* the *Kabala,* and Greek philosophy, but what about Indian philosophy, Yoga and Taoism? What were the original teachings? How can they be practiced today? What is the source of pain and suffering in the world and what is the solution? Discover the deepest mysteries of the mind and universe within and outside of your self. 8.5" X 11" ISBN: 1-884564-01-1 Soft $19.95

2.   EGYPTIAN YOGA: African Religion Volume 2- Theban Theology U.S. In this long awaited sequel to *Egyptian Yoga: The Philosophy of Enlightenment* you will take a fascinating and enlightening journey back in time and discover the teachings which constituted the epitome of Ancient Egyptian spiritual wisdom. What are the disciplines which lead to the fulfillment of all desires? Delve into the three states of consciousness (waking, dream and deep sleep) and the fourth state which transcends them all, Neberdjer, "The Absolute." These teachings of the city of Waset (Thebes) were the crowning achievement of the Sages of

Ancient Egypt. They establish the standard mystical keys for understanding the profound mystical symbolism of the Triad of human consciousness. ISBN 1-884564-39-9 $23.95

3. THE KEMETIC DIET: GUIDE TO HEALTH, DIET AND FASTING Health issues have always been important to human beings since the beginning of time. The earliest records of history show that the art of healing was held in high esteem since the time of Ancient Egypt. In the early 20th century, medical doctors had almost attained the status of sainthood by the promotion of the idea that they alone were "scientists" while other healing modalities and traditional healers who did not follow the "scientific method' were nothing but superstitious, ignorant charlatans who at best would take the money of their clients and at worst kill them with the unscientific "snake oils" and "irrational theories". In the late 20th century, the failure of the modern medical establishment's ability to lead the general public to good health, promoted the move by many in society towards "alternative medicine". Alternative medicine disciplines are those healing modalities which do not adhere to the philosophy of allopathic medicine. Allopathic medicine is what medical doctors practice by an large. It is the theory that disease is caused by agencies outside the body such as bacteria, viruses or physical means which affect the body. These can therefore be treated by medicines and therapies The natural healing method began in the absence of extensive technologies with the idea that all the answers for health may be found in nature or rather, the deviation from nature. Therefore, the health of the body can be restored by correcting the aberration and thereby restoring balance. This is the area that will be covered in this volume. Allopathic techniques have their place in the art of healing. However, we should not forget that the body is a grand achievement of the spirit and built into it is the capacity to maintain itself and heal itself. Ashby, Muata ISBN: 1-884564-49-6 $28.95

4. INITIATION INTO EGYPTIAN YOGA Shedy: Spiritual discipline or program, to go deeply into the mysteries, to study the mystery teachings and literature profoundly, to penetrate the mysteries. You will learn about the mysteries of initiation into the teachings and practice of Yoga and how to become an Initiate of the mystical sciences. This insightful manual is the first in a series which introduces you to the goals of daily spiritual and yoga practices: Meditation, Diet, Words of Power and the ancient wisdom teachings. 8.5" X 11" ISBN 1-884564-02-X Soft Cover $24.95 U.S.

5. *THE AFRICAN ORIGINS OF CIVILIZATION, RELIGION AND YOGA SPIRITUALITY AND ETHICS PHILOSOPHY* HARD COVER EDITION Part 1, Part 2, Part 3 in one volume 683 Pages Hard Cover First Edition Three volumes in one. Over the past several years I have been asked to put together in one volume the most important evidences showing the correlations and common teachings between Kamitan (Ancient Egyptian) culture and religion and that of India. The questions of the history of Ancient Egypt, and the latest archeological evidences showing civilization and culture in Ancient Egypt and its spread to other

countries, has intrigued many scholars as well as mystics over the years. Also, the possibility that Ancient Egyptian Priests and Priestesses migrated to Greece, India and other countries to carry on the traditions of the Ancient Egyptian Mysteries, has been speculated over the years as well. In chapter 1 of the book *Egyptian Yoga The Philosophy of Enlightenment,* 1995, I first introduced the deepest comparison between Ancient Egypt and India that had been brought forth up to that time. Now, in the year 2001 this new book, *THE AFRICAN ORIGINS OF CIVILIZATION, MYSTICAL RELIGION AND YOGA PHILOSOPHY,* more fully explores the motifs, symbols and philosophical correlations between Ancient Egyptian and Indian mysticism and clearly shows not only that Ancient Egypt and India were connected culturally but also spiritually. How does this knowledge help the spiritual aspirant? This discovery has great importance for the Yogis and mystics who follow the philosophy of Ancient Egypt and the mysticism of India. It means that India has a longer history and heritage than was previously understood. It shows that the mysteries of Ancient Egypt were essentially a yoga tradition which did not die but rather developed into the modern day systems of Yoga technology of India. It further shows that African culture developed Yoga Mysticism earlier than any other civilization in history. All of this expands our understanding of the unity of culture and the deep legacy of Yoga, which stretches into the distant past, beyond the Indus Valley civilization, the earliest known high culture in India as well as the Vedic tradition of Aryan culture. Therefore, Yoga culture and mysticism is the oldest known tradition of spiritual development and Indian mysticism is an extension of the Ancient Egyptian mysticism. By understanding the legacy which Ancient Egypt gave to India the mysticism of India is better understood and by comprehending the heritage of Indian Yoga, which is rooted in Ancient Egypt the Mysticism of Ancient Egypt is also better understood. This expanded understanding allows us to prove the underlying kinship of humanity, through the common symbols, motifs and philosophies which are not disparate and confusing teachings but in reality expressions of the same study of truth through metaphysics and mystical realization of Self. (HARD COVER) ISBN: 1-884564-50-X $45.00 U.S.   81/2" X 11"

6. AFRICAN ORIGINS BOOK 1 PART 1 African Origins of African Civilization, Religion, Yoga Mysticism and Ethics Philosophy-Soft Cover $24.95 ISBN: 1-884564-55-0

7. AFRICAN ORIGINS BOOK 2 PART 2 African Origins of Western Civilization, Religion and Philosophy (Soft) -Soft Cover $24.95 ISBN: 1-884564-56-9

8. EGYPT AND INDIA AFRICAN ORIGINS OF Eastern Civilization, Religion, Yoga Mysticism and Philosophy-Soft Cover $29.95 (Soft) ISBN: 1-884564-57-7

9. THE MYSTERIES OF ISIS: **The Ancient Egyptian Philosophy of Self-Realization** - There are several paths to discover the Divine and the mysteries of the higher Self. This volume details the mystery teachings of the goddess Aset (Isis) from Ancient Egypt- the path of wisdom. It includes the teachings of her temple and

the disciplines that are enjoined for the initiates of the temple of Aset as they were given in ancient times. Also, this book includes the teachings of the main myths of Aset that lead a human being to spiritual enlightenment and immortality. Through the study of ancient myth and the illumination of initiatic understanding the idea of God is expanded from the mythological comprehension to the metaphysical. Then this metaphysical understanding is related to you, the student, so as to begin understanding your true divine nature. ISBN 1-884564-24-0 $22.99

10. EGYPTIAN PROVERBS: collection of —Ancient Egyptian Proverbs and Wisdom Teachings -How to live according to MAAT Philosophy. Beginning Meditation. All proverbs are indexed for easy searches. For the first time in one volume, ——Ancient Egyptian Proverbs, wisdom teachings and meditations, fully illustrated with hieroglyphic text and symbols. EGYPTIAN PROVERBS is a unique collection of knowledge and wisdom which you can put into practice today and transform your life. $14.95 U.S   ISBN: 1-884564-00-3

11. GOD OF LOVE: THE PATH OF DIVINE LOVE The Process of Mystical Transformation and The Path of Divine Love   This Volume focuses on the ancient wisdom teachings of "Neter Merri" –the Ancient Egyptian philosophy of Divine Love and how to use them in a scientific process for self-transformation. Love is one of the most powerful human emotions. It is also the source of Divine feeling that unifies God and the individual human being. When love is fragmented and diminished by egoism the Divine connection is lost. The Ancient tradition of Neter Merri leads human beings back to their Divine connection, allowing them to discover their innate glorious self that is actually Divine and immortal. This volume will detail the process of transformation from ordinary consciousness to cosmic consciousness through the integrated practice of the teachings and the path of Devotional Love toward the Divine. 5.5"x 8.5" ISBN 1-884564-11-9 $22.95

12. INTRODUCTION TO MAAT PHILOSOPHY: Spiritual Enlightenment Through the Path of Virtue   Known as Karma Yoga in India, the teachings of MAAT for living virtuously and with orderly wisdom are explained and the student is to begin practicing the precepts of Maat in daily life so as to promote the process of purification of the heart in preparation for the judgment of the soul. This judgment will be understood not as an event that will occur at the time of death but as an event that occurs continuously, at every moment in the life of the individual. The student will learn how to become allied with the forces of the Higher Self and to thereby begin cleansing the mind (heart) of impurities so as to attain a higher vision of reality. ISBN 1-884564-20-8 $22.99

13. MEDITATION The Ancient Egyptian Path to Enlightenment   Many people do not know about the rich history of meditation practice in Ancient Egypt. This volume outlines the theory of meditation and presents the Ancient Egyptian Hieroglyphic text which give instruction as to the nature of the mind and its three modes of expression. It also presents the texts which give instruction on the

practice of meditation for spiritual Enlightenment and unity with the Divine. This volume allows the reader to begin practicing meditation by explaining, in easy to understand terms, the simplest form of meditation and working up to the most advanced form which was practiced in ancient times and which is still practiced by yogis around the world in modern times. ISBN 1-884564-27-7 $22.99

14. THE GLORIOUS LIGHT MEDITATION TECHNIQUE OF ANCIENT EGYPT New for the year 2000. This volume is based on the earliest known instruction in history given for the practice of formal meditation. Discovered by Dr. Muata Ashby, it is inscribed on the walls of the Tomb of Seti I in Thebes Egypt. This volume details the philosophy and practice of this unique system of meditation originated in Ancient Egypt and the earliest practice of meditation known in the world which occurred in the most advanced African Culture. ISBN: 1-884564-15-1 $16.95 (PB)

15. THE SERPENT POWER: The Ancient Egyptian Mystical Wisdom of the Inner Life Force. This Volume specifically deals with the latent life Force energy of the universe and in the human body, its control and sublimation. How to develop the Life Force energy of the subtle body. This Volume will introduce the esoteric wisdom of the science of how virtuous living acts in a subtle and mysterious way to cleanse the latent psychic energy conduits and vortices of the spiritual body. ISBN 1-884564-19-4 $22.95

16. EGYPTIAN YOGA *The Postures of The Gods and Goddesses* Discover the physical postures and exercises practiced thousands of years ago in Ancient Egypt which are today known as Yoga exercises. Discover the history of the postures and how they were transferred from Ancient Egypt in Africa to India through Buddhist Tantrism. Then practice the postures as you discover the mythic teaching that originally gave birth to the postures and was practiced by the Ancient Egyptian priests and priestesses. This work is based on the pictures and teachings from the Creation story of Ra, The Asarian Resurrection Myth and the carvings and reliefs from various Temples in Ancient Egypt 8.5" X 11" ISBN 1-884564-10-0 Soft Cover $21.95 Exercise video $20

17. SACRED SEXUALITY: EGYPTIAN TANTRA YOGA: The Art of Sex Sublimation and Universal Consciousness This Volume will expand on the male and female principles within the human body and in the universe and further detail the sublimation of sexual energy into spiritual energy. The student will study the deities Min and Hathor, Asar and Aset, Geb and Nut and discover the mystical implications for a practical spiritual discipline. This Volume will also focus on the Tantric aspects of Ancient Egyptian and Indian mysticism, the purpose of sex and the mystical teachings of sexual sublimation which lead to self-knowledge and Enlightenment. 5.5"x 8.5" ISBN 1-884564-03-8 $24.95

18. AFRICAN RELIGION Volume 4: ASARIAN THEOLOGY: RESURRECTING OSIRIS The path of Mystical Awakening and the Keys to Immortality NEW

REVISED AND EXPANDED EDITION!   The Ancient Sages created stories based on human and superhuman beings whose struggles, aspirations, needs and desires ultimately lead them to discover their true Self. The myth of Aset, Asar and Heru is no exception in this area. While there is no one source where the entire story may be found, pieces of it are inscribed in various ancient Temples walls, tombs, steles and papyri. For the first time available, the complete myth of Asar, Aset and Heru has been compiled from original Ancient Egyptian, Greek and Coptic Texts. This epic myth has been richly illustrated with reliefs from the Temple of Heru at Edfu, the Temple of Aset at Philae, the Temple of Asar at Abydos, the Temple of Hathor at Denderah and various papyri, inscriptions and reliefs.   Discover the myth which inspired the teachings of the *Shetaut Neter* (Egyptian Mystery System - Egyptian Yoga) and the Egyptian Book of Coming Forth By Day. Also, discover the three levels of Ancient Egyptian Religion, how to understand the mysteries of the Duat or Astral World and how to discover the abode of the Supreme in the Amenta, *The Other World*   The ancient religion of Asar, Aset and Heru, if properly understood, contains all of the elements necessary to lead the sincere aspirant to attain immortality through inner self-discovery. This volume presents the entire myth and explores the main mystical themes and rituals associated with the myth for understating human existence, creation and the way to achieve spiritual emancipation - *Resurrection.* The Asarian myth is so powerful that it influenced and is still having an effect on the major world religions. Discover the origins and mystical meaning of the Christian Trinity, the Eucharist ritual and the ancient origin of the birthday of Jesus Christ. Soft Cover ISBN: 1-884564-27-5 $24.95

19.   THE EGYPTIAN BOOK OF THE DEAD MYSTICISM OF THE PERT EM HERU " I Know myself, I know myself, I am One With God!–From the Pert Em Heru "The Ru Pert em Heru" or "Ancient Egyptian Book of The Dead," or "Book of Coming Forth By Day" as it is more popularly known, has fascinated the world since the successful translation of Ancient Egyptian hieroglyphic scripture over 150 years ago. The astonishing writings in it reveal that the Ancient Egyptians believed in life after death and in an ultimate destiny to discover the Divine. The elegance and aesthetic beauty of the hieroglyphic text itself has inspired many see it as an art form in and of itself. But is there more to it than that? Did the Ancient Egyptian wisdom contain more than just aphorisms and hopes of eternal life beyond death? In this volume Dr. Muata Ashby, the author of over 25 books on Ancient Egyptian Yoga Philosophy has produced a new translation of the original texts which uncovers a mystical teaching underlying the sayings and rituals instituted by the Ancient Egyptian Sages and Saints. "Once the philosophy of Ancient Egypt is understood as a mystical tradition instead of as a religion or primitive mythology, it reveals its secrets which if practiced today will lead anyone to discover the glory of spiritual self-discovery. The Pert em Heru is in every way comparable to the Indian Upanishads or the Tibetan Book of the Dead $28.95."   ISBN# 1-884564-28-3 Size: 8½" X 11

20.   African Religion VOL. 1- ANUNIAN THEOLOGY THE MYSTERIES OF RA The Philosophy of Anu and The Mystical Teachings of The Ancient Egyptian Creation Myth Discover the mystical teachings contained in the Creation Myth and the gods and goddesses who brought creation and human beings into existence. The Creation myth of Anu is the source of Anunian Theology but also of the other main theological systems of Ancient Egypt that also influenced other world religions including Christianity, Hinduism and Buddhism. The Creation Myth holds the key to understanding the universe and for attaining spiritual Enlightenment. ISBN: 1-884564-38-0 $19.95

21.   African Religion VOL 3: Memphite Theology: MYSTERIES OF MIND Mystical Psychology & Mental Health for Enlightenment and Immortality based on the Ancient Egyptian Philosophy of Menefer -Mysticism of Ptah, Egyptian Physics and Yoga Metaphysics and the Hidden properties of Matter.   This volume uncovers the mystical psychology of the Ancient Egyptian wisdom teachings centering on the philosophy of the Ancient Egyptian city of Menefer (Memphite Theology). How to understand the mind and how to control the senses and lead the mind to health, clarity and mystical self-discovery. This Volume will also go deeper into the philosophy of God as creation and will explore the concepts of modern science and how they correlate with ancient teachings. This Volume will lay the ground work for the understanding of the philosophy of universal consciousness and the initiatic/yogic insight into who or what is God? ISBN 1-884564-07-0 $22.95

22.   AFRICAN RELIGION VOLUME 5: THE GODDESS AND THE EGYPTIAN MYSTERIESTHE PATH OF THE GODDESS THE GODDESS PATH The Secret Forms of the Goddess and the Rituals of Resurrection The Supreme Being may be worshipped as father or as mother. *Ushet Rekhat* or *Mother Worship*, is the spiritual process of worshipping the Divine in the form of the Divine Goddess. It celebrates the most important forms of the Goddess including *Nathor, Maat, Aset, Arat, Amentet and Hathor* and explores their mystical meaning as well as the rising of *Sirius,* the star of Aset (Aset) and the new birth of Hor (Heru). The end of the year is a time of reckoning, reflection and engendering a new or renewed positive movement toward attaining spiritual Enlightenment. The Mother Worship devotional meditation ritual, performed on five days during the month of December and on New Year's Eve, is based on the Ushet Rekhit. During the ceremony, the cosmic forces, symbolized by Sirius - and the constellation of Orion ---, are harnessed through the understanding and devotional attitude of the participant. This propitiation draws the light of wisdom and health to all those who share in the ritual, leading to prosperity and wisdom. $14.95 ISBN 1-884564-18-6

23.   *THE MYSTICAL JOURNEY FROM JESUS TO CHRIST* Discover the ancient Egyptian origins of Christianity before the Catholic Church and learn the mystical teachings given by Jesus to assist all humanity in becoming Christlike. Discover the secret meaning of the Gospels that were discovered in Egypt. Also discover

how and why so many Christian churches came into being. Discover that the Bible still holds the keys to mystical realization even though its original writings were changed by the church. Discover how to practice the original teachings of Christianity which leads to the Kingdom of Heaven. $24.95   ISBN# 1-884564-05-4 size: 8½" X 11"

24.   THE STORY OF ASAR, ASET AND HERU: An Ancient Egyptian Legend (For Children)   Now for the first time, the most ancient myth of Ancient Egypt comes alive for children. Inspired by the books *The Asarian Resurrection: The Ancient Egyptian Bible* and *The Mystical Teachings of The Asarian Resurrection, The Story of Asar, Aset and Heru* is an easy to understand and thrilling tale which inspired the children of Ancient Egypt to aspire to greatness and righteousness. If you and your child have enjoyed stories like *The Lion King* and *Star Wars you will love The Story of Asar, Aset and Heru.* Also, if you know the story of Jesus and Krishna you will discover than Ancient Egypt had a similar myth and that this myth carries important spiritual teachings for living a fruitful and fulfilling life. This book may be used along with *The Parents Guide To The Asarian Resurrection Myth: How to Teach Yourself and Your Child the Principles of Universal Mystical Religion.* The guide provides some background to the Asarian Resurrection myth and it also gives insight into the mystical teachings contained in it which you may introduce to your child. It is designed for parents who wish to grow spiritually with their children and it serves as an introduction for those who would like to study the Asarian Resurrection Myth in depth and to practice its teachings. 8.5" X 11"   ISBN: 1-884564-31-3 $12.95

25.   THE PARENTS GUIDE TO THE AUSARIAN RESURRECTION MYTH: How to Teach Yourself and Your Child the Principles of Universal Mystical Religion. This insightful manual brings for the timeless wisdom of the ancient through the Ancient Egyptian myth of Asar, Aset and Heru and the mystical teachings contained in it for parents who want to guide their children to understand and practice the teachings of mystical spirituality. This manual may be used with the children's storybook *The Story of Asar, Aset and Heru* by Dr. Muata Abhaya Ashby.   ISBN: 1-884564-30-5 $16.95

26.   HEALING THE CRIMINAL HEART. Introduction to Maat Philosophy, Yoga and Spiritual Redemption Through the Path of Virtue   Who is a criminal? Is there such a thing as a criminal heart? What is the source of evil and sinfulness and is there any way to rise above it? Is there redemption for those who have committed sins, even the worst crimes?   Ancient Egyptian mystical psychology holds important answers to these questions. Over ten thousand years ago mystical psychologists, the Sages of Ancient Egypt, studied and charted the human mind and spirit and laid out a path which will lead to spiritual redemption, prosperity and Enlightenment.   This introductory volume brings forth the teachings of the Asarian Resurrection, the most important myth of Ancient Egypt, with relation to the faults of human existence: anger, hatred, greed, lust, animosity, discontent, ignorance, egoism jealousy, bitterness, and a myriad of psycho-spiritual ailments

which keep a human being in a state of negativity and adversity   ISBN: 1-884564-17-8 $15.95

27. TEMPLE RITUAL OF THE ANCIENT EGYPTIAN MYSTERIES--THEATER & DRAMA OF THE ANCIENT EGYPTIAN MYSTERIES: Details the practice of the mysteries and ritual program of the temple and the philosophy an practice of the ritual of the mysteries, its purpose and execution. Featuring the Ancient Egyptian stage play-"The Enlightenment of Hathor' Based on an Ancient Egyptian Drama, The original Theater -Mysticism of the Temple of Hetheru 1-884564-14-3 $19.95 By Dr. Muata Ashby

28.   GUIDE TO PRINT ON DEMAND: SELF-PUBLISH FOR PROFIT, SPIRITUAL FULFILLMENT AND SERVICE TO HUMANITY Everyone asks us how we produced so many books in such a short time. Here are the secrets to writing and producing books that uplift humanity and how to get them printed for a fraction of the regular cost. Anyone can become an author even if they have limited funds. All that is necessary is the willingness to learn how the printing and book business work and the desire to follow the special instructions given here for preparing your manuscript format. Then you take your work directly to the non-traditional companies who can produce your books for less than the traditional book printer can. ISBN: 1-884564-40-2 $16.95 U. S.

29. Egyptian Mysteries: Vol. 1, Shetaut Neter What are the Mysteries? For thousands of years the spiritual tradition of Ancient Egypt, *Shetaut Neter,* "The Egyptian Mysteries," "The Secret Teachings," have fascinated, tantalized and amazed the world. At one time exalted and recognized as the highest culture of the world, by Africans, Europeans, Asiatics, Hindus, Buddhists and other cultures of the ancient world, in time it was shunned by the emerging orthodox world religions. Its temples desecrated, its philosophy maligned, its tradition spurned, its philosophy dormant in the mystical *Medu Neter*, the mysterious hieroglyphic texts which hold the secret symbolic meaning that has scarcely been discerned up to now. What are the secrets of *Nehast* {spiritual awakening and emancipation, resurrection}. More than just a literal translation, this volume is for awakening to the secret code *Shetitu* of the teaching which was not deciphered by Egyptologists, nor could be understood by ordinary spiritualists. This book is a reinstatement of the original science made available for our times, to the reincarnated followers of Ancient Egyptian culture and the prospect of spiritual freedom to break the bonds of *Khemn,* "ignorance," and slavery to evil forces: *Såaa* . ISBN: 1-884564-41-0 $19.99

30.   EGYPTIAN MYSTERIES VOL 2: Dictionary of Gods and Goddesses This book is about the mystery of neteru, the gods and goddesses of Ancient Egypt (Kamit, Kemet). Neteru means "Gods and Goddesses." But the Neterian teaching of Neteru represents more than the usual limited modern day concept of "divinities" or "spirits." The Neteru of Kamit are also metaphors, cosmic principles and vehicles for the enlightening teachings of Shetaut Neter (Ancient Egyptian-

African Religion). Actually they are the elements for one of the most advanced systems of spirituality ever conceived in human history. Understanding the concept of neteru provides a firm basis for spiritual evolution and the pathway for viable culture, peace on earth and a healthy human society. Why is it important to have gods and goddesses in our lives? In order for spiritual evolution to be possible, once a human being has accepted that there is existence after death and there is a transcendental being who exists beyond time and space knowledge, human beings need a connection to that which transcends the ordinary experience of human life in time and space and a means to understand the transcendental reality beyond the mundane reality. ISBN: 1-884564-23-2 $21.95

31.   EGYPTIAN MYSTERIES VOL. 3 The Priests and Priestesses of Ancient Egypt This volume details the path of Neterian priesthood, the joys, challenges and rewards of advanced Neterian life, the teachings that allowed the priests and priestesses to manage the most long lived civilization in human history and how that path can be adopted today; for those who want to tread the path of the Clergy of Shetaut Neter. ISBN: 1-884564-53-4 $24.95

32.   The War of Heru and Set: The Struggle of Good and Evil for Control of the World and The Human Soul This volume contains a novelized version of the Asarian Resurrection myth that is based on the actual scriptures presented in the Book Asarian Religion (old name –Resurrecting Osiris). This volume is prepared in the form of a screenplay and can be easily adapted to be used as a stage play. Spiritual seeking is a mythic journey that has many emotional highs and lows, ecstasies and depressions, victories and frustrations. This is the War of Life that is played out in the myth as the struggle of Heru and Set and those are mythic characters that represent the human Higher and Lower self. How to understand the war and emerge victorious in the journey o life? The ultimate victory and fulfillment can be experienced, which is not changeable or lost in time. The purpose of myth is to convey the wisdom of life through the story of divinities who show the way to overcome the challenges and foibles of life. In this volume the feelings and emotions of the characters of the myth have been highlighted to show the deeply rich texture of the Ancient Egyptian myth. This myth contains deep spiritual teachings and insights into the nature of self, of God and the mysteries of life and the means to discover the true meaning of life and thereby achieve the true purpose of life. To become victorious in the battle of life means to become the King (or Queen) of Egypt.Have you seen movies like The Lion King, Hamlet, The Odyssey, or The Little Buddha? These have been some of the most popular movies in modern times. The Sema Institute of Yoga is dedicated to researching and presenting the wisdom and culture of ancient Africa. The Script is designed to be produced as a motion picture but may be addapted for the theater as well. $21.95   copyright 1998 By Dr. Muata Ashby ISBN 1-8840564-44-5

33.   AFRICAN DIONYSUS: FROM EGYPT TO GREECE: The Kamitan Origins of Greek Culture and Religion ISBN: 1-884564-47-X   FROM EGYPT TO GREECE This insightful manual is a reference to Ancient Egyptian mythology and

philosophy and its correlation to what later became known as Greek and Rome mythology and philosophy. It outlines the basic tenets of the mythologies and shoes the ancient origins of Greek culture in Ancient Egypt. This volume also documents the origins of the Greek alphabet in Egypt as well as Greek religion, myth and philosophy of the gods and goddesses from Egypt from the myth of Atlantis and archaic period with the Minoans to the Classical period. This volume also acts as a resource for Colleges students who would like to set up fraternities and sororities based on the original Ancient Egyptian principles of Sheti and Maat philosophy. ISBN: 1-884564-47-X $22.95 U.S.

34. THE FORTY TWO PRECEPTS OF MAAT, THE PHILOSOPHY OF RIGHTEOUS ACTION AND THE ANCIENT EGYPTIAN WISDOM TEXTS ADVANCED STUDIES This manual is designed for use with the 1998 Maat Philosophy Class conducted by Dr. Muata Ashby. This is a detailed study of Maat Philosophy. It contains a compilation of the 42 laws or precepts of Maat and the corresponding principles which they represent along with the teachings of the ancient Egyptian Sages relating to each. Maat philosophy was the basis of Ancient Egyptian society and government as well as the heart of Ancient Egyptian myth and spirituality. Maat is at once a goddess, a cosmic force and a living social doctrine, which promotes social harmony and thereby paves the way for spiritual evolution in all levels of society. ISBN: 1-884564-48-8 $16.95 U.S.

35. **THE SECRET LOTUS:** *Poetry of Enlightenment*
Discover the mystical sentiment of the Kemetic teaching as expressed through the poetry of Sebai Muata Ashby. The teaching of spiritual awakening is uniquely experienced when the poetic sensibility is present. This first volume contains the poems written between 1996 and 2003. **1-884564--16 -X $16.99**

Order Form

Telephone orders: Call Toll Free: 1(305) 378-6253. Have your AMEX, Optima, Visa or MasterCard ready.

Fax orders: 1-(305) 378-6253   E-MAIL ADDRESS: Semayoga@aol.com

Postal Orders: Sema Institute of Yoga, P.O. Box 570459, Miami, Fl. 33257. USA.

Please send the following books and / or tapes.

ITEM

_____Cost $_____

_____Cost $_____

_____Cost $_____

_____Cost $_____

_____Cost $_____

Total $_____

Name:_____

Physical Address:_____

City:_____ State:_____ Zip:_____

Sales tax: Please add 6.5% for books shipped to Florida addresses

_____Shipping: $6.50 for first book and .50¢ for each additional

_____Shipping: Outside US $5.00 for first book and $3.00 for each additional

_____Payment:_____

_____Check -Include Driver License #:

_____

_____Credit card: _____ Visa, _____ MasterCard, _____ Optima,
_____ AMEX.

Card number:_____

Name on card:_____ Exp. date:_____/_____

Copyright 1995-2005 Dr. R. Muata Abhaya Ashby
Sema Institute of Yoga
P.O.Box 570459, Miami, Florida, 33257
(305) 378-6253 Fax: (305) 378-6253